Chinese Mosaic
(NEW EDITION)

中國故事
(新版本)

Shaio Shen Yu 于孝慎

Writers' Branding
1800-608-6550
www.writersbranding.com
orders@writersbranding.com

Contents

Section One-

Memoirs, Escape Stories, Short Stories, Essays

A Dream

I had a dream to be a writer ever since I was five years old in 1945. My eldest sister gave me a picture book about an orphaned little bird seeking friends. She taught me to read word by word. I recited it before I slept and I read it to my imaginary friend, a home-made rag doll which Wong Ma made for me. So my sister told me that I should learn to write stories like it and that's the beginning of my ever present dream of being a writer. I want to write books, to be a writer. I had won composition contests during my school years in Taiwan and a short story contest in a university in Colorado. For nine years, I had a column in a Colorado newspaper-Pueblo Chieftain. However, I want to write books and also memoirs for the posterity. I thought about it often but procrastination always won. There were so many excuses not to write the book that I had dreamed to write; *I'm busy now, I'll wait until my children grow up, I'll wait until I'm retired*, or simply *I am not in the mood to write*. It goes on and on. Sure, I did start to write it at different times. I bought fancy notebooks, I bought a laptop, and I bought colorful mechanical pencils…but I failed to keep it up. The thought of writing have been lingering on in my mind. It's like breathing, consciously or unconsciously, I know it is there and I cannot and wish not to ignore it.

All the excuses of not to write became ridiculous and nonexistent after I retired. I adopted a new stratagem that was to enroll in writing classes. I hope that the group support and the instructor's guidance will help me to write. It did not work. I was patronized and, I hope it was unintentionally, insulted by my fellow classmates twice. They simply assumed that I, a senior Chinese woman, can only know

1

little or minimum English. One asked me, "You come to the wrong class. We write in English. " and another one kindly suggested that I should record my story on tapes and ask someone else to write it for me. I don't think they realized that I had been accepted into the class the same way they did. I had to submit a piece of my writing for the instructor to review before he/she would accept me as a student. I felt like crying; and I almost wanted to forgo my dream of writing even though the instructors of both the writing classes liked what I wrote and encouraged me to write more.

I did not write for two years because I thought that my knowledge of the English language must be indeed inadequate as those two classmates from the writing classes presumed. I had to realize it that writing in English must be an impossible dream for me and it's no use to pursue it. I read a lot instead and sometime I felt a tinge of regret of not writing. I told myself that I will write later when my English is better. My dream of being a writer was like a piece of ember, flickering but was never completely out. I would go about the uneventful daily life routinely. Only when something drastic happened and life had dealt me a deadly bolt; I had cancer in 2006. I realize that my personal supply of tomorrows is no longer limitless. I do not have the luxury of time; I resolved to write as soon as I am well again.

My two daughters and my three half-Chinese grandchildren do not know and speak Chinese. I write the Chinese stories in English. This book is the beginning of the realization of my dream. These stories are written randomly, not chronically, and are not limited to my own life. Some of them are fictional pieces based on the true lives of my friends, or inspired by hearsays about my contemporaries. Some of them are historical stories. I dotted each story with bits of Chinese history and customs. I hope whoever reads them will know more about me, my generation, my family, and my people, the Chinese. I will continue to build and fulfill my dream of writing. I had, and have, a dream. I am glad that I have one.

–End-

My birthday

I am not an April fool and I am no fool.

I know myself and so does almost everyone who knows me will definitely agree that I am no fool. But I am an April fool. My 'official and reported' birthday is April 1, 1939. Either the date or the year is correct. I was born on the first day of the 4th month of the lunar calendar. It could be any date in between March and May of the Gregorian (solar) calendar.

The lunar calendar is based on the observation of the moon. The interval from new moon to new moon is about 29 and one-half days, so a lunar month would be either 29 or 30 days. There are twelve months, 354.36 days in a year, almost 11 days shorter than a year in a solar calendar.

The Chinese lunar year has to be adjusted to the solar year and the actual farming seasons by the addition of one whole month every 3 or 5 years. The system was established in China around 500 B.C. One month, either 30 or 29 days, has to be added on every three years or two months to be added on during a five-year circle. A total of seven months (210 days) must be added every 19 years. Coincidentally, the ancient Greek lunar Calendar, which was founded about 400 B.C., also had 354.30 days in a year.

Except the 1st.9th and 12th months, any of the other nine months can be an additional month during a leap year. The system is very complicated; only the astrologers can decide which year will be the leap year and which month will have the extra one.

I was born in a backward and old fashioned village in the Japanese occupied North China, 3 years after the Nanjing Massacre (1937) when Japanese killed 3 million Chinese in a few weeks. I was also considered one year old the first day I was born in line with the centuries-old Chinese tradition. There was no newspaper and radio in the village. My father, a Japanese university graduate, was captured by the Japanese army to be an interpreter a few months before I was born. The exact "hour, date and year ' of my birth varies; it depends on whoever told the story. My mother, without my father with her, was too busy to keep all her children, 7 of them before I was born, safe from the Japanese soldiers, the Chinese communists, and bandits. Besides, I was an unwanted girl child and the least of her attention. My most reliable information regarding my 'Date of birth' came from my eldest sister; she was 16 at that time. She and my father agreed that I was born in 1940.

In 1949, my family escaped from Communist China to Taiwan and most of the birth records were lost during the long escape. I was 9 years old, but my family registered me as 10 years old in order to get more food vouchers. So I am one year younger than my official birth date.

I was born on the 1st day of the fourth month and I remembered that I had two birthdays in 1963 in Taiwan. In 1982, I should have had two birthdays also, but I did not know since I forgot to check the dates on the Chinese calendar. Officially, April 1st is my birthday, but I always try to tell people that I'm not a fool.

The Chinese lunar calendar is widespread in the Far East. The Chinese New Year and other festivals are always simultaneously observed in Japan, Korea and many other countries in Asia.

-End-

My First Home

Samha Street, Jinan, Shandong, N. China—1941-1944

(山東省濟南市三和街)

I was born in the Yu village in Shandong where my father was born. When I was one and half years old, we moved to Jinan, the capital of Shandong Province, in northern China. My first home in Jinan was a one-story mud and brick building that stood alongside a long, narrow yard. My family lived there until I was almost five years old.

I do not remember if there were connecting doors between the rooms. I do know that each room had a door which opened to the yard. The kitchen and the outhouse were almost on the opposite ends of the long yard, and a gate was at the end of Samha Street (三和街). My sisters and brothers attended Samha Elementary School (三和街小学). When I was visiting Jinan, china in 2014, the school is still there.

A man came every morning to draw water from the well for our family. He covered the well with planks afterwards and I was threatened with a heavy spanking if I ever went near to it. I was the youngest of seven children, and often played by myself under a big tree at a corner. I was told that I did not wear diapers during the day and there was a long slit in my pants so that I could squat and pee. My 2nd oldest sister, 12 years older than me, told me that I was quite naughty. She recalled that one of my favorite games was

5

to drown the ants with my own urine or to torture the ants with a twig. I don't remember whether we had a dog or not, but I know that we had chickens. Once, I tried to pull a pretty feather off a rooster's tail and it bit me.

My parents ordered us, my siblings and me, to go to bed when it was getting dark. There were black drapes on all the windows. Paper strips were taped onto the glass to prevent the glasses from shattering during the bombing. The Japanese had built some heavy industries to manufacture necessary supplies around Jinan; the American and Chinese air forces tried to bomb them. My older sister told me years later that our neighbors had mixed feelings about the bombing at that time; they were afraid of the air attacks, but wished the Japanese would be killed and defeated soon.

We dreaded the night, and the fear of darkness stayed with me all the time. My bed was actually a huge basket upon a makeshift low bench in my parents' room. As soon as the first siren sounded, my father would turn off the dim light in the room. We waited in the dark and sometimes we could hear the muffled sounds of explosion and gunfire. The residential areas were seldom hit and the industrial area was outside of the city gate.

My mother had four boys and three girls before I was born. My birth was considered a surplus. In my family, my birth year is an unsolved mystery: was it the year of Dragon--1940 or the year of Hare--1939? My father and two of my older sisters all insisted that I was born in 1940, but my mother thought it was 1939. My mother insisted, '*I was forty-two when XiaoYar (小丫 little girl, that's me) was born and I should know.*' The way she counted her age was based on the old Chinese custom that a newborn would be one-year old at birth. The superstitious idea behind that system of calling a day-old baby as one-year old was that a one-year old child would be bigger and heavier and no evil spirit could take the baby's life away easily. Along that same way of thinking was to call a strong boy baby a weak girl baby aloud so that the evil spirit would not be jealous enough to snatch the boy away. My mother was highly educated but she was a stickler for old traditions. One of my brothers explained, '*You are not the only one who is a year*

6

older than you really are. So are our eldest sister and our eldest brother. The three of you were born in the backward village, while the rest of us were born in either Jinan or Tsingtao (two big cities in Shandong) where newspaper were available.' Anyway, I was born in the earlier part of the Sino-Japanese War when the Japanese invaded Northern China.

The war officially started in 1937 when the Japanese fought the Chinese army at Marco Polo Bridge (蘆溝橋) adjacent to Beijing. The Chinese suffered terrible defeats. The drawn-out conflicts with the warlords and the Chinese Communists after the fall of the Qing Dynasty (清朝) in 1911 had weakened Chiang Kai-shek's Nationalist government. After the Nanjing Massacre in December 1937, when the Japanese army killed thousands of Chinese, the Chinese government retreated to Szechuan and the southwest part of China. The Japanese seized Northern China and rewarded the Chinese who willingly surrendered with high positions to help them govern the Chinese.

My father was a Japanese-educated architect and he spoke Japanese fluently. Before the war, he had a very good position in Jinan and built a three-story family home with almost my mother's rich dowry. The Japanese recruited him with the promise of a high position. My father refused, he did not want to be a traitor. It was not safe for him to stay in Jinan. When he knew that a high-ranked Japanese officer coveted his house, he and some other loyal Chinese civil services workers left Jinan to join the retreating government, and sent my mother and the children back to my paternal grandpa's home in the country. My mother often bitterly reminisced about the frequent terrible, dangerous situations she had to face without my father.

It was perilous for a woman to travel through the Japanese-occupied area and the robber-infested countryside, and my mother endured this journey with only her children by her side. Many years later when I learned about the Japanese soldiers' atrocious crimes during the war in my history class, I asked my eldest sister about that particular trip. She told me, *'It was terrible. The sloshing snow soaked through our cloth shoes. Mother did not allow us to wear leather shoes. We had to take the train part of the way and there were many Japanese soldiers on that train. I was almost 14 and your second oldest sister was 9. Mother dressed us as boys and herself as a man. We were frightened. We heard that the Japanese had raped many Chinese women from 8 to 60 years old in Nanjing two months ago (December 1937). Your youngest brother, the one who died shortly after you were born, cried all the time. He thought mother and his nanny, dressed in men's clothes, were strangers. My girlfriend's sister-in-law was raped and killed in a village not far from Jinan. We were lucky that a German priest, Father Croft, helped us get on the crowded train. Everyone wanted to get out of Jinan.* 'For their safety, my father had arranged a trusted friend and two stalwart servants to escort my mother's entourage.

My paternal grandpa arranged nice living quarters for my mother and the children, but my mother did not get a warm welcome from her mother-in-law. My mother lamented often, '*your grandma never liked me, just because I have big feet.*' My maternal grandpa was a man of foresight. He knew the world was changing and did not want my mother to have her feet bound. He also taught her how to read and write. So, my mother was one of hundreds of women with unbound feet and an education, in Northern China in 1938. Shanghai and other cities had long begun the 'feet free' movement.

My mother was different and an oddity in a world where the 'Golden Lilies', a poetic term for small bound feet, was the irrefutable symbol of a woman's beauty and virtue. On the account of her big feet, the distinguished Confucius family chose my mother's homely cousin to be their daughter-in-law, even though my mother was the prettier one. She married my father, an overseas student in Japan, who actually thought that '*foot-binding*' was cruel and old-fashioned. Mother said more than once, '*My big feet had seen us through many difficult times.*' Actually, my mother had relatively small feet. She wore size-five shoes.

It was a dangerous period before I was born. The Japanese had only superficial control of the cities. Chinese guerrillas, Chinese Communists and bandits were everywhere in the country. My grandpa and other landowners were their targets of extortion. No

8

one was safe. My 3rd sister, who was six years old at that time, told me that one night my family was under attack and the house was on fire. She remembered that my mother shouted, '*Run, run to the woods and hide!*' When it was over, my mother was crying and the damage was extensive. Luckily my mother and her trusted maid had buried valuables at different places and my family was all right again. My sister told me my grandpa praised my mother, '*Clever and tough.*' Even my grandma started to warm up to my mother.

With more dogs, the neighborhood organized their own protection group and my 13 year-old big brother and other boys started to stand watch at dusk. Some older neighbors taught the boys martial arts. My mother also started to urge my elder siblings to resume their studies, and she began to teach the younger ones how to read and write. A few months later, my father came back. That's how I was born in the village at my grandmother's home, where my father was born.

My mother suffered postpartum depression after I was born. There was no doctor, only a midwife to assist her and it was a difficult birth. She was exhausted and unhappy with her life in general at that time and she was not used to fewer servants. I was told that she seemed not to care too much about me and she did not have milk. My two eldest sisters, who were 12 and 16 years old, and the servants raised me. Later my eldest sister often teased, '*Xiao Yar (little girl), you better behave and obey me. You wouldn't be here today if I did not take care of you when you were a baby.*' And I was repeatedly told that I was darker while my three sisters all have my mother's fair complexion because the woman they hired to nurse me was dark-complexioned. Actually I took after my father who was darker. The woman who nursed me did not have enough milk for her son, who was a few months older than me, but I thrived on mush mixed with yolk and smashed vegetable. There was not too much baby fat on me and I was not cute. I was told that my grandpa was the only one who liked me. Being another girl, I was a disappointment to my mother and the whole family. My father was the fourth son. His three older brothers were either deceased or had no young children any more. My 5th and 6th uncles passed away. Three of my father's younger brothers were away fighting the Japanese somewhere. I was the newest addition to a family full of girls and I was the 15th granddaughter.

There was another tragedy. When I was almost one year old, my 3 years old brother and I were both sick with diarrhea. He died and I lived. He was the second son my mother had lost. All my life I've lived under the impression that my mother, who preferred to have a son than a daughter, had wished that I was the one who died. My 3rd oldest sister told me that she feels the same way as I do since my mother lost a boy a year older than her.

My brother's death woke my mother from her depression and she started to pay more attention to my care. When she found a tiny dot in the center of my palm, she got a doctor immediately. It was a case of blood poisoning. The blind Chinese doctor ordered to have a cow killed and covered my hand and arm with slices of the cow's liver, and to feed me with freshly squeezed watermelon juice. It was in the middle of winter and it cost a lot to acquire the cow and the watermelon that some rich landowner from another village kept in the cellar. I was cured. In 1947 before we left Jinan for Taiwan, the blind doctor escaped from the country and my mother must have helped him to settle in Jinan. She said, "Dr. Lee saved your life," and ordered me to kowtow trice to the doctor.

The Japanese authority hanged a few soldiers who had raped the Chinese women and put down some bandits to protect the Chinese civilians. They also encouraged the growth of new business and manufacture. My father returned to Jinan alone and was employed by the Red Swastika Society 世界紅卍字會. It was founded in China in 1922; it is an organization similar to the Red Cross. He designed and built a magnificent, palatial building. The building is now the Shandong Provincial Museum.

1942 was the second time my mother had to travel with seven children alone. She had to go back to Jinan where my father was busy working. I was told that it was also a dangerous trip. The Chinese underground resistance force had ripped apart a section of the railroad. It was about a half-mile long. Only a handful of Japanese soldiers were on guard against the possible attack from the Chinese guerrilla. My family had to run to catch the train at the other part. My mother often told us, "*I could not run fast if I do not have big feet.*"

Finally we joined my father at the rented house on Samha Street, where we lived until I was almost five years old. We were poor but my mother immediately hired a tutor to teach my elder siblings. My eldest sister studied hard and my mother paid fifty dollars a month, a big chunk of my father's salary, for her to attend a private parochial school, instead of the Japanese-run public schools. The Japanese forced the Chinese to learn Japanese in school from 3rd grade and up.

My mother often emphasized the importance of having 'a good n education', especially for the girls. She often said, "*To have a good education is the key to have a career and to be independent.*" Before she passed away at 99 years old in Colorado, she mentioned that she was very pleased that she has one doctor and two teachers among her 4 daughters.

When I was four years old, my 9 years old bad-tempered brother caught tetanus and he almost died. My mother stayed in the hospital with him for many days and she was elated that she did not lose another son. When he was convalescing, we the children, especially me, were told repeatedly that we could not irate him in any way. My mother truly spoiled him and he became abusive to all of us, and I, being 5 years younger than he, became his easy target of abuse. When I think about my childhood, the constant fear of this abusive brother comes often to my mind and it surely dimmed my memory of my childhood.

-End-

Sheujai Garden, Jinan 1944-1945
徐家花園, 山東省, 濟南市

I did not know the street address of the second house I had lived in Jinan when I was 4 years old. It was called Sheujai Garden and we did not live there very long. After the Japanese surrender in the fall of 1945, we moved back to the three-story modern home that my father had built before I was born.

The house at Sheujai Garden was a typical home in Northern China at that time. There were rooms on four sides of a walled square yard with a gate opened into a laneway or a street. There was no well when we first moved in but later there was a well with a pump. A kitchen and an outhouse were on the opposite corner of the rooms along the west wall. There was a special room with a big drawing table and swinging lamps where my father taught architect draftsmanship and design. Two or three students came to study. My father gained recognition after he built the palace styled buildings for the Red Swastika Society and a stylish Jinan Municipal Hospital. I was not allowed to go in or even near to that classroom but the two students brought me goodies sometimes.

We moved there shortly after my youngest brother got well from tetanus. It was late spring in 1944. My 3rd elder sister was 13 years old and a typical tomboy. She was not tall enough to ride my father's bike properly but she rode it anyway with me sitting on the handle bar and pots and pans hanging over the sides. Half way to the new house she lost control over a curve and fell. Luckily we both were not hut but I cried, actually yelled. My sister told me not to cry and threatened me into secrecy or else she would leave me there. Year later we both laughed when we reminisced.

There were Japanese soldiers all over the city and none of the children were allowed to go anywhere far from the house after schools. We did not have so many black outs and air attacks as we had a year before. My sister told me that the "war front" was father to the south and the Chinese, with American's help, was the war against Japanese. "Very soon, "She said, "The Japanese will be defeated and we can move back to the big house."

Our new home at Sheujai Garden must be not far from Samha St. where my first home was. My siblings attended Samha Elementary School and a high school close to it. My 2nd elder sister was a first year student at an elementary school teacher's training school and she would be an elementary school teacher. My eldest sister attended a medical college and lived in the dormitory. She came home only on some weekends. I was left alone again during the school days to entertain myself with chickens and ants again. I remembered that I did not mind it at all. Actually it was a kind of relieve from constant fear of my 9 years old abusive brother. I sang the songs that my 2nd sister taught me and me recited lines of the classic poems which my mother enjoyed reading aloud. They were poems written by Li Po李白 of the Tan唐 Dynasty in the 10th century. I also made up ridiculous stories to tell Wong Ma and Lee Ma who cooked for us.

There was another piece of childhood memory that made me a laughingstock. My father's youngest brother, my 9th uncle stayed with us for a while. He was a humorous man and often made everyone laugh when the family sat together to have supper. One evening he tasted a dish and then said aloud, *Lee Ma killed the salt peddler!"* I jumped down from the chair and ran out of the gate because I wanted to be the first one, before my brother, to see the dead peddler and the policeman. I had heard so many talks about the war and the killings and I did not want to miss the chance to wee a dead person. I heard my mother calling me to stop but I kept running. Wong Ma, who had her feet bound, could not run after me. My 2nd elder sister caught me. She told me that no one was killed. It was my 9th Uncle' way to say that Lee Ma must have plenty salt to use

13

to make that dish so salty. Everyone laughed, even my stern father laughed. My name had an additional word added on afterwards, now everyone called me Ban笨(stupid) 小丫, instead of Xiao Yar 小丫. In 1952 I was a first year junior high student in Taiwan. One of my classmates lived nearby overheard my 3rd sister calling me Ban Xiao Yar. I was a kind of an odd celebrity in school for a short while and I was very embarrassed

There were hardly any snakes in Northern China, but I thought that I saw one at our home in Shujar Garden that winter and no one believed me. I was sick, probably chicken pox, and my mother moved me into a corner room with an extra charcoal burner to keep me warm. Wong Ma also put a bunch of yellow soft newly hatched chickens in the same room to keep them warm. I was alone sleeping on the bed and I saw the head of a snake coming out of a hole at the corner and snatched one of the baby chickens. I yelled and my mother and the adults rushed in but they saw nothing. They thought the hole was too small and they were not quite sure of the numbers of the baby chickens. So they did not believe me and thought I was delirious from the fever. My father examined the tiny hole and said that he would hire someone to seal it soon. In a few days I was getting better and the baby chickens grew fast and you can see the beginning of the short wing started to grow. Then it happened again. I yelled and this time the snake could not drag the growing baby chicken through the hole, the chicken lost a wing and was bleeding. My father hired someone to put on extra plaster in every corner of every room and he believed that I saw a rat, not a snake.

Then it was springs and it got warmer and I grew taller and I could sing more songs. My mother was considering enrolling me in a kindergarten. I passed the entrance examination. and the teachers at the kindergarten told my mother that I was very smart. The money was tight and I could not go. Everything cost more and there were food shortage, fuel shortage everywhere. The Chinese-Japanese war had been almost eight years. (1937 t0 1944) and the WWII was in the 4th year.

Everyone talked about the Japanese imminent defeat and the end of the war. We had a good radio and I remembered that some neighbors came at night to listen to it. One of the neighbors, Uncle Chen who understood English, told everyone that the Russian had defeated the German army and the English and American army had pushed the aggressive German back. My father listened to the Japanese broadcast and told my mother that; the more the Japanese bragged about their military victory the more he could tell that the Japanese were losing the war. There were rumors that many small groups of Japanese soldiers were ambushed and killed by the Chinese underground resistance forces. There were riots in the city and some bold Chinese would jeered at the Japanese openly and the Japanese women dared not going out. Mother was talking about keep my sisters from school but she did not want them to be behind their schooling either since the school year was almost ended. Anyhow she kept everyone at home after school.

There were talks about the United States' continuous bombing of Tokyo and the mainland Japan. We knew the Japanese would soon be defeated, too. When we heard that the United States dropped two atomic bombs on Japan shortly before the start of the new school year. My sisters, brothers and their friends all threw their Japanese books out. They shouted "We don't have to learn Japanese anymore!"

One day my father came home early and told us excitedly, "The Japanese surrendered! We finally won the war." Almost every day and on every street the folks were laughing and celebrating and it was the Chinese people's turn to jeer at, or even beat up, the defeated Japanese who had not fled back to Japan fast enough.

We moved back to our three-story home as soon as the Japanese who lived there went away. I started Grade I at Samha Elementary School in Sept, 1945.

-End-

Wang Ma 王媽 and the Nanjing Massacre南京大屠殺

I was, and was definitely not, an orphan. I had parents, three elder brothers and three elder sisters. Now at 79, I'm privileged to have two elder sisters and one elder brother here in the United States. However I felt like, and lived as, an orphan when I was almost five in 1945, the year the Japanese surrendered and the eight-year long Sino-Japanese war ended. We were in Japanese occupied Jinan, North China. My wealthy and high-born mother, had a hard time adjusting to the harsh life with seven children and I was the unwanted last child. My mother was depressed all the time and my two elder sisters more or less took care of me. Also, my mother preferred sons. My youngest elder brother, who was 5 years older than me, had just recovered from tetanus and my mother favored him and spoiled him so much that he became my most feared abuser. I remember that I even dared not cry and hid in the kitchen with Lee Ma 李媽 when he was around. Lucky for me, Wang Ma 王媽 came into my life and she cared for me so much that I wished she were my real mother.

My oldest sister attended a Catholic pre-med school and a tall erman Father was my father's friend. One day, a black-robed Catholic nun brought Wang Ma王媽 to my home. An ugly dark purple scar ran from Wang Ma's eye to her chin and made her face look lopsided and her right eye could hardly open. I cried at first sight of her. Lee Ma took me aside. She dried my tears and gave me a piece of cake and told me that the evil Japanese killed Wang

Ma's family and made her look terrible. I should be nice to Wang Ma who had no home now.

I knew what Lee Ma meant by the "evil Japanese". Two years before I was born, the Japanese had occupied Jinan and most of the east coast of China. We children were told that the Japanese soldiers were cruel, and they would beat up the Chinese at any time, any place with hardly any reason at all. The Japanese killed thousands and thousands of Chinese, and they also hurt and drugged many Chinese for medical research in Manchuria. We were all afraid of the Japanese. Sometimes my sister would take me to the school playground to play. On our way there, we had to pass a building with Japanese soldiers on guard. I always shivered with fear and dared not look at the Japanese soldiers' shining bayonets.

My three sisters and three brothers all went to school during the day and I had no one to play with besides Lee Ma. Lee Ma told me that I should be glad to have Wang Ma around now.

I recalled that I complained, "She talks funny."

Lee Ma explained that Wang Ma王媽 was from Nanjing, quite far to the South from Jinan. The people there talk that way. If we were to go there, the folks there would think we talk funny.

*Neon*娘 (my mother) hired Wang Ma王媽. We called any woman helper "Ma"媽. After her last name. We, the northern Chinese call mother "Neon" and the southerners call mother "Ma". Wang Ma looked sad and she was always busy washing clothes for the whole family. She walked to the community well to draw water when my older brothers were not around to get the water for us. She balanced a long bamboo pole with two pails hanging at each end on her bony shoulders, and walked with a crablike gait on her bound feet. *Neon* (mother) was the only woman I knew at that time who did not have her feet bound. Sometimes I walked on my heels behind Wang Ma and imitated the way she walked. She knew it and she was never mad at me, even though I was afraid she might yell at me like Lee Ma did whenever I did the same thing with her. Instead, Wang Ma was very nice to me and made sure that my face and clothes were clean and looked at me fondly and made a beautiful rag doll for me to play with. I really liked her and I knew that she was sad. So,

I tried to help her with the laundry, but the cold water made my fingers numb.

Wang Ma soon realized that I was scared of my abusive brother and she made sure that I wasn't alone when he was around. She would hold me when I cried and once I felt her tears on me and I asked her why. She told me she had a daughter a little older than me, who was killed by the Japanese. She took it upon herself to care for me, bathe me, comb my hair, and cut my nails. Once when I was sick with a high fever, she soothed my face with cold towels. I followed her everywhere and she even let me trace the scar on her face.

*Baba*爸爸 (my father) was a Japanese-educated architect and he did not want to work for the Japanese. I remember that we were poor and the house was small. Lee Ma lived not far from us and she went home every night. My three brothers shared one room, and my sisters and I shared another room. Mother let Wang Ma王媽 share the bedroom with my sisters and let me sleep on a small bed in her room. One night I was in bed holding the rag doll Wang Ma made for me. I heard my mother tell my father that Wang Ma cut her face up herself so that the Japanese would not hurt her and Wang Ma sometimes cried in her sleep. *Baba* sighed. They talked about arranging a marriage between Dr. Chen's one-armed servant Chang and Wang Ma. Many years had gone by before I finally realized that Wang Ma had to cut her own face lest the Japanese would rape her. My mother did not want me to hear the word "rape" on that night.

Mother warned us not to ask Wang Ma about her past. She said something like this: "*We all know it was bad and we should not make her sad all over again.*" However, I was puzzled at that time so I thought, '*Wang Ma is afraid that the Japanese will hurt her. She must be afraid of the pain and then she cut her own face up. It must be very, very painful, too. So why did she do it?*' I asked my 17-year-old sister. She told me that 7 years ago (1937) the Japanese had killed thousands and thousands of Chinese in Nanjing. Wang Ma's husband and children were among the victims. It was called the Nanjing massacre. She then warned me to keep quiet. She said, "Don't ever tell anybody. The Japanese do not want anyone to know

18

about it." I knew the Japanese forced the Chinese to learn Japanese in school from 3rd grade and up. They also taught the students the distorted and fictitious history of the war between the Chinese and the Japanese. They denied that they invaded China and declared instead that the Chinese had provoked the war. Anyway that cold spring in 1945 was the last spring that the Japanese occupied China. Wang Ma grated her teeth angrily whenever the word Japanese was mentioned.

Summer was approaching quickly. One afternoon, Lee Ma and Wang Ma were busy talking and sewing new summer clothes, while I was squatting and torturing the ants. I did not fully understand what they were talking about, but I knew that Lee Ma must have advised Wang Ma that she should let the past go and be happy. Wang Ma indicated that she did not want to return to the South or anywhere close to Nanjing. When Wang Ma started to sob, Lee Ma stood up, took me to the kitchen and told me something like this, "*Shiao Yar*, we don't want to embarrass her. Let's pretend that we did not see her cry."

One day my father came home early and told us excitedly, "The Japanese surrendered! We finally won the war." Almost every day, and on every street, the folks were laughing and singing about winning the 8-year-long war with the Japanese. It was the Chinese people's turn to jeer at, or even beat up, the defeated Japanese who had not fled back to Japan fast enough. *Baba* (father) told us that the Chinese, especially the survivors of the Nanjing Massacre who had fled to the north, hated the Japanese so much that the streets in Jinan were in chaos. The Chinese beat up any Japanese they saw, even the women and the children. It got so bad that some respected Chinese elders had to come out to restrain the mobs. *Neon* (mother) kept us all at home. Anyway, everyone was busy packing and excited that we finally could move back to the three-story mansion *Baba (father)* built as soon as the Japanese who lived there went away.

Baba (father) got a very good position and *Neon* (mother) hired more servants. Wang Ma got married, so we should have called her Chang Ma, but we still called her Wang Ma. She and her husband both worked for us and she looked happy. Oh! She was so pretty wearing my mother's old cloths. She sewed pretty new dresses for me and she told me many, many stories when she walked me to and from school. She was not very skinny anymore; even the scar on her face seemed lighter. I spent a lot of time with them; and her husband, Chang *Ba* (uncle), carried me often with his one arm and gave me many piggyback rides. I was very happy and I wished that time would stand still.

Unfortunately, the civil war between Chiang Kai-shek's Nationalists and Mao Tse-tung's Communists intensified. The victorious Communists seized Mainland China. My family and all the people who disagreed with the Communists became frightened and left mainland China for Taiwan in 1949. Wang Ma and Lee Ma remained in Mainland China. It was heart wrenching when we parted. Until now whenever I think about or hear the word 'mother' mentioned, I always feel guilty for thinking of Wang Ma first instead of my own mother. Wang Ma was the one who gave me a true mother's love and I was blessed that I had her unconditional love for a most treasured four years. I miss Wang Ma very much and I often dream of Lee Ma and the scar-faced Wang Ma, my dearest

-End-

**Historical Note, Sino-Japanese war started in 1937, four years before WWII. In December 1937, the Japanese raped and killed thousands of Chinese women from 8 years old to 60 years old. A total of three hundred thousand Chinese were massacred at Nanjing in a period of several weeks.

Wars

"*Mom, have you ever been in a war? Sergeant Donavan is coming to my class to tell us something about wars.*" my second-grade daughter asked me while I watched her younger sister tie her shoelaces. I thought, '*Have I ever?*' My throat tightened.

"*Mom?*" She pouted and impatiently whined.

Looking at her smooth small face, I hesitated to put any smudge of fear on it. It would be cruel to shock her sweet innocence with the grisly truth about wars.

I hugged them and lied, "*No. I am not a soldier. I never fought in a war. When I was your age, there were wars everywhere in China. I'm lucky that I have not been in a war zone. I pray that you and your sister will never be close to where there will be a war.*"

How could I tell them about the two wars I had experienced before I was eight years old? I decided to write something about my traumatic war experiences as a part of my legacy.

The first one.

I was born in Shandong Province, China during the war between the Chinese and Japanese. When I was one year old, Japan attacked Pearl Harbor and the already four-year long Sino-Japanese War became the Second World War.

My father was a Japanese educated architect. He went to Japan when he was only 14 years old. He spoke Japanese fluently. In 1940, the Japanese army captured him and forced him to be an interpreter. My mother and the whole household went into hiding in the country after the news of the Nanjing massacre reached north China. I was told that I was born in the village and my father was not present.

21

Of course I was only an infant then, and I could not have remembered or have known anything about the war. However, I remembered the feelings of constant fear. The sounds of the barking dogs at twilight and the loud gunshot when the Japanese killed the barking dogs, stayed with me always. Even now I do not like to go out at night. At that time, my nanny was about twenty. She and my three-year-old brother's nanny had a perpetual fear of being raped by the Japanese soldiers. They never undressed and even kept their shoes on in bed at night. When there was a warning signal that the Japanese were coming, sometimes they would gather the children to hide in a hollowed spot in a heap of hay close to the outhouse. My nanny often stretched her hand over my mouth keep me from crying when the Japanese soldiers thrust their bayonets into the hay. I shudder whenever I remember that I was told that once the sharp point of a bayonet narrowly missed my nanny's left ear. For a long time I would tremble with fear whenever I heard dogs bark at twilight.

Another unfortunate event of my life is also associated with that war. The sanitary condition in the country was poor at that time. My three years old brother and I both caught diarrhea. My nanny boiled the food, dishes, and chopsticks before she fed me and her son, but my brother's nanny did not. So, my brother died and I lived. In a male-oriented society, my mother preferred a son to a daughter. My brother's death cast a permanent shadow on my life when I am made to believe, that my mother often wished that my brother should be the one to have lived, not me.

After the Japanese completed the occupation of Northern China, my father was released and we lived in the city of Jinan under the Japanese's harsh control. I remember that my sisters and I would walk the long way to avoid passing the Japanese soldiers on guard duty at some buildings. If we ever had to pass the soldiers, I always lowered my head and tried not to look at the soldiers and their bayonets. Sometimes I dreamed about the bayonets.

The second one.

World War II ended. There were gala celebrations everywhere and the Japanese were gone in 1945. For the Chinese, the civil war between Chang Kai-shek's Nationalist Party and Mao Tse-tung's Communist Party intensified. For me, my second war experiences were actually the continuation of the first one. The only difference was that the Chinese soldiers were fighting with each other.

The war came close to Jinan and I heard more and more talks of war when I started the second grade in 1947. Everyone tried to flee from the impending battle over the city of Jinan, a strategic military point. My father and my older siblings all escaped to Shanghai and then Taiwan. Mother and I stayed behind with my dearest Wong Ma to close the sale of the mansion.

When the siege of Jinan started, we were trapped. The airport was closed, the railroad services stopped. Wang Ma and her husband took us to his home in the country to hide. There, we could hear the constant low roars of the cannons. As children, we stood by the country lanes and watched the groaning wounded soldiers on makeshift stretchers pass by. The dripping blood and the loose dirt formed small red pea-sized balls. Some boys picked them up and smelled them. Later I learned that I had lived through one of the bitterest battles between the two parties.

Once, a piece of stray shrapnel scraped just above my left ear when we escaped from one village to the other. The sound of cannon and gunfire were close and loud, I was so paralyzed with fear that I did not know I had been wounded until later Wong Ma told my mother that there was caked blood on the tip of my ear and the matted hair. My family believed that I had ten lives, one more than a cat might have.

The fighting lasted almost six weeks. It ended when the victorious Communist Party seized the city. On the way back to our house, we had to walk through streets that were scattered everywhere with dead soldiers. I remembered that I screamed and screamed when I had to step over a black bloody stub of a single leg with one high boots up to the knee. My mother slapped me hard to quiet me. I became numb and walked through and stepped over pools of black blood, bodies, and broken limbs and my eyes burned from the stench.

In 1948, we finally reached Taiwan and lived in peace. No more wars, but the horrifying memories of wars buried deep in me and will never die.

-End-

Escape from the 'Siege' of Jinan(濟南), Shandong, China, 1948

From my memory

World War II (1941-1945), eight years long Sino-Japanese war (1937-1945) for the Chinese, ended in September 1945 when the Japanese surrendered. There were gala celebrations everywhere, and the defeated Japanese were gone. At the same time, the civil war between Chang Kai-shek's 蔣介石 Nationalist Party and Mao Tse-tung's 毛澤東 Communist Party intensified. Now the Chinese soldiers were fighting with each other. My 8th uncle was in the Nationalist army. My 7th uncle was a communist before the war. He defected from the Communist party in 1946 and was on Communist's priority hit list. In 1947, he was in hiding somewhere and dared not go back to his wife and children in Jinan. We heard more and more of Communist's atrocities. My paternal grandfather only had a few acres of war wasted farmland. Communists hanged him. My one-eyed and tall 9th uncle hid in the middle of a draining ditch with my ninety years old grandmother on his shoulders. With help from a trusted tenant, his family and my grandmother escaped to Jinan. They lived in my father's resident quarter in the Jinan Paper Factory. My father was the vice president since he understood read all the documents written in Japanese. My 8th uncle's wife and two daughters also escaped and stayed with us. I had two first cousins just about my age to play with me.

The civil war came close to Jinan, and I heard more and more talks of war when I started the 2nd grade in 1947. Communists gained most of the countryside, and only the big cities were still in the Nationalist's hand. Everyone tried to flee from the impending battle over the city of Jinan, a strategic military and railroad center. There were Nationalists' soldiers stationed in our backyard and empty spaces between the houses. My father and three of my older siblings all left for Shanghai, and then Taiwan. My mother and I stayed behind to close the sale of the house. When the siege of the city of Jinan become imminent in August 1948, we were trapped. There were no airport and railroad services. Wang Ma, who was a second mother to me, left for the village with her new husband. I cannot remember where my two cousins went, nor the how and when mother and I moved to the Paper factory. Now I am writing events that happened seventy-two years ago, the years passed by fast as flowing current of the river, and carried away details.

Japanese, who had occupied Jinan since 1937, built the Paper factory complex cannon-proof, bomb-proof secure during WWII. We, many families, fled from the imminent 'siege' of Jinan, slept on the floors of the offices as well the storage areas, or even between the standing still machines. Someone must have organized a mess kitchen to provide us meals. Rumors, rumors were many. It reported that, with the city dwellers' full support, the Nationalists army could repel the Communist' attack or even push them back to the north. Then the bad news, a Nationalist general and his company defected to the Communist lest they would hang his father. It might put the Paper Factory in the direct line of fire. One of my father's former students worked as a truck driver for the Paper Factory. He drove my family out to his home far out in the country to wait out the war. There, we could hear the constant low roars of the cannons. As children, we stood by the country lanes and watched the groaning wounded Communists soldiers on makeshift stretchers pass by. The dripping blood and the loose dirt formed small red pea-sized balls. Some boys picked them up and smelled them. Years later, I learned that I had lived through one of the critical battles between the two parties.

Once, a piece of stray shrapnel scraped just above my left ear when we escaped on foot from one village to the other. The sound of cannon and gunfire was close and loud, and I was too scared to know that I was wounded. Later that night, my mother noticed the caked blood on the tip of my ear and the matted hair. My family believed that I had ten lives, one more than a cat might have.

The fighting lasted almost six weeks, and the final siege took place for more than a week. It ended when the victorious Communist Party seized the city. My 9th uncle and grandmother went back to their home at the Paper Factory, which had only a little damage. The city streets were full of debris and roadblocks, and the truck could not drive through. Mother and I had to walk through streets that were scattered everywhere with dead soldiers. I remembered that I screamed and screamed when I had to step over a black, bloody stub of a single leg with one high boot up to the knee. My mother slapped me hard to quiet me. I became numb and walked through and stepped over pools of black blood, bodies, and broken limbs, and my eyes burned from the stench.

We were in shock to find out that six families lived in our house. It was similar to the scene which depicted many families who shared his family home in Moscow in the movie "Doctor Zhivago." My mother had to negotiate, even beg them to vacant one room only for both of us to live without our nice beds. We shared meals with everyone in the communist lifestyle. A Communist comrade (同志tóng zhì) told my mother that I must be back to school, and I did. The portraits on the honorable place –the center of the front wall of all the classrooms were now Mao Zedong (毛澤東) and Zhou Enlai(周恩來). They must have burned or thrown away the ones of Chang Kai shik (蔣介石)and stored somewhere the ones of Sun yet sen (孫中山), the founder of the Republic China. The Communists also respect him. We had a new teacher. She was a Communist comrade; she taught us the latest dance and song 'the East Is Red' (东方红),' and words to praise the Chinese Communist.

One day my dearest Wang Ma and her husband came to visit. She brought me new warmer clothes, shoes, with the material recycled from my mother's old garments that my mother had given her. She also cut my finger and toenails for the last time. It was a final goodbye. We all knew that we would never see each other again, and I could not cry when she held me tight before she left. I was sick, no fever but silent and listless for a while. My mother got permission from the Communist comrade to allow me to stay home.

The city of Jinan was short of food, fuel, housing, and other life commodities. To save food and resources, the new Communist government encouraged seniors, women, and children to leave Jinan. I remembered that my mother took me with her and walked to different offices and talked to different people. She also brought, more likely, exchanged with something she had, some food so we could eat away from home. My mother was the owner of the big house, and we were considered the 'bad' property owner.' The communists ordered us to eat with other families who lived in our big house. We were not allowed to have food in the one-room we were allowed to live. In retrospect, I knew that my mother must have been busy to arrange the trip.

One early morning in November, my mother pulled a sleepy me to walk to the sidewalk of a wide street. Two trucks came, and a black-robed Catholic father held me up on a truck full of older men, women, and children. I had just managed to sit beside my mother; the truck drove out. Some people sat on the floor on the covered bed of the truck. I remembered that some men had complained that they could not stretch their legs. The canvas cover was full of bullet holes, and it flapped in the cold wind. I was cold and hungry, but I kept quiet. I knew that my mother brought no food. A woman, a distant relative, gave me some coarse, but so delicious to me, dried cakes to eat. She must be poor and was allowed to have her kitchen.

It was a hand crinkled and war-scarred army truck. The going was slow on the uneven road full of cannon holes. When it stopped somewhere to refill the gas, the village or town folks would sell us some hard-boiled eggs. It rumored that there were occasional battles fought between the Communist army, and some hide-out defeated the Nationalist army. Once, we had to hide in a patch of wood to wait out one of the supposed skirmishes. It was not safe to drive in the dark, so we slept on the floor in a classroom of a rural school. Finally, we reached the Nationalist government, controlled Qingdao, and met with my 2nd sister. My mother and I had a much needed two weeks long rest at my maternal uncle's place. We had new heavy winter clothes. The best thing was that we took off the shoes to go to bed at night since there was no need to be ready to run at any hour. It was the only time that my mother indulged me in eating all kinds of delicacies she bought with the money which she had withdrawn from a British bank. We all knew that the Communist army would soon size Qingdao. So, we sailed to Shanghai as quickly as possible and finally reached free Taiwan in 1949.

-End-

Escape- the final journey from Shanghai to Taiwan, 1949

From my memory

From my memoryI had the first sight of the trees covered island Taiwan in the spring of 1949 when I tiptoed and leaned on the railings of the ship. There were five thousand refugees from Shanghai on board. I sensed from my sister's trembling, restraining hand, and her suddenly relieved sigh that our long-time fear was evaporating. We were finally safe!!! And no more "Escape." I was almost ten years old, and we would live in peace ever after. I am eighty years old now, and a resident of a safe and secured assisted living facility in the U.S., and WWII had been three-quarters of a century down the history. Sometimes my fear of the twilight, the darkness, dog barking still stay with me and comes in my nightmares. From three years before I was born up to I was ten, my family and many other Chinese families experienced hair-raising 'escapes episodes.' Many families were separated: wives and children left behind on mainland China. My dearest Wong Ma, a servant who had been almost a mother to me for more than four years, could not come with us to Taiwan. Many men married again in Taiwan because the wives and children were lost or separated. The government and the general public agreed that this act of second marriage was a regrettable but unavoidable necessity.

I can't remember the month now, but I recall that we dressed up too warm for a sunny day when we disembarked on the port Keelung, *Taiwan (基隆, 台灣). My father went to Taiwan earlier.*

He wrote to us that there was no need for heavy winter clothes in Taiwan. Taiwan is close to the equator and is very warm. Anyway, my mother insisted that we wore thick cotton-padded long coats and pants and shoes. It got warmer three days on the sea after we sailed south from Shanghai (上海), but Mother forbade us to take off the clumsy winter clothes even when we have to fight our way to get meals.

The ship named was Diamond金鋼輪 (literary gold and steel, diamond) was a modern and luxury ocean liner. It and its other two sister ships transporting the mass Chinese war refugees to Taiwan from Shanghai. Shanghai was full of Chinese from different provinces tried to escape the imminent Communist occupation of the whole mainland. At that time, Chairman Mao's Communist army already occupied most parts of China. Shanghai had high inflation. It would cost a big bamboo basketful paper money to buy one GIN (斤 1.2 lb) of rice. Mother must have paid with gold for three of us a triple bunk bed in the congested cargo area of the ship. She also must have spent a lot to hire two men to help us to fight our way to get on the ship.

I remembered that I was on one of the man's shoulders. The man told me to hold on his neck tight because he had to carry some luggage with one hand and pulled my 2nd sister along with the other hand. The other man must have half carried, and half dragged my mother along. There were so many people pushed around and fought each other to get on the ship. The ship officers who were trying to collect tickets soon lost control. It was chaos, and I was scared. Many other Chinese elders and children could not get on the ship. The two men were only supposed to get us past the tickets checkpoint, but they did not stop, or maybe they could not turn around to get down the gangway anymore. So they dragged us to our assigned triple bunk beds along the wall. It was lucky for us because later, the passengers could not get their designated beds because some stowaways already occupied the beds. Some passengers slept on the floor. I could not recall when and how the two men finally left the ship and back to Shanghai to their families. My father and two brothers, one sister, had to sleep on the deck two nights to wait for the ship to go to Taiwan eight months before. My father had to carry my short fourteen years old brother on his shoulders, drag my 3rd sister and 2nd brother, and elbowed his way to get on the ship. They lost most of the luggage. He then wrote to my mother, "buy the cheapest beds but pay well for two men to help you." The scene in the movie "Dr. Zhivago," that depicted that his family fought to get on the train at Moscow resembled my experience of getting on the ship in Shanghai.

My memory of those six to eight days on the ship to Taiwan 70 years ago is blurred. The boat finally departed from Shanghai in the late afternoon. Mother and I were seasick. I remembered that Mother vomited a couple of times, and I just slept most of the time the next day. My usually active mother hardly ever left her narrow lower level of the triple bunk bed. I was in the upper one, and my sister had the middle one. There were no curtains or any kind of divider between the beds. Every day at noon, I followed my sister to get our portion of the food and drinking water for one day. The routine was that I stood in line, and my sister took two trips to carry the food staff back to our beds. We had to walk up to the upper deck to use the temporarily screened off lavatory area with pails and no divided stalls. We could also stand in line to use the ship's restroom with flushing toilets.

When I think back about that trip, I realized that we were fortunate. The couple on the bunk beds across from us took us under their wings when they knew that we were alone, a mother and two girls. We had problems with communication, they spoke Shanghainese, and we spoke Mandarin. My mother did not stop me when I talked to them and answered their questions freely without any reservation. They were also going to Taiwan, and they were not communist comrades who would trick me into telling them about my family. They, especially the woman, liked me, and she taught me some tricks with fingers and strings. She gave me a chocolate bar, and I nibbled on it to make it last. Also, we were lucky to have sunny and calm days. There were no storms, no rain. We could have fresh air upon the promenade deck, away from the foul odor of seasick and unwashed bodies in the cargo hold where we slept. Somehow

I remembered the best was the seemingly connected pure blue sky and blue sea with scattered pieces of cotton-like clouds above.

I was not bored on the ship, and the best part of it was the feelings of 'being safe.' Of course, we still slept full clothes since there was no privacy, but we no longer need to wear shoes. When I took off my shoes to sleep, I enjoyed the happy thought that my mother would not shake me up at any hour, because we had to move to another safer place. We all knew that we would be safe in Taiwan. Even we, the children, heard enough and understood the cheerful talk. 'Sure. Taiwan is safe. The presence of the United States Navy's 7th Fleet in the Taiwan Strait will keep Mao Tze-tung from overtaking Taiwan."

There was no pushing, angry shouting, fighting when we disembarked at Keelung, Taiwan. Instead, some passengers had cheerfully assisted the elders and children. It was high noon and hot, we carried our heavy topcoats while some kind passengers helped us with our luggage. Father and my 2nd brother were waiting for us at the end of the gangway. Right there, I had the most embarrassing moment of my short life. Mother undressed right there in public. OH! We are laughingstocks! I lowered my head and dared not to look. To my surprise that I heard no snicker and some other women were taking off their long pants, too. The women who came from Northern China took off their heavy padded pants just like Mother did. The women from Southern China also took off their lighter weight long pants. I dared not to ask when my parents were busy. Later my sister explained, "They had to! They were afraid of being robbed. Mother had sewed many pieces of gold in the lining of her pants. We also had some gold rings hidden in our pants." I finally understood why Mother was always in bed and moved so slow. She carried extra weight! In 1950, Taiping (太平輪), another cross-strait steamer bound for Keelung from Shanghai sunk. It had carried too much gold. Salvage teams from Japan, Taiwan, and Communist China are still trying to find the ship and the treasure.

My 1st sister, 25 years old, and a medical doctor, arrived in Taiwan with her husband and her newborn son with the medical group. My brother, 24 years old and a university student, got to

Taiwan with the students' group. Mother was so happy to have all her seven children together. We lived in Taiwan with no need to escape anymore. I grew up in Taiwan, attended schools, and later taught schools until I left Taiwan when I was 26 years old.

-End-

My Mother's Big Feet

One Saturday morning in November 1992, I sat on a stool beside my mother's feet to sew strips of red ribbons on a pair of slippers as shoelaces. The pair of size five black satin slippers I bought at Kmart was too big for my mother, even though they were the smallest sized ones I could find. My mother sighed and reminisced as she had over the years, the same lament. *"When I was young, everyone laughed at my big ugly feet. My mother couldn't find me a husband before I was twenty-one, and later my mother-in-law had never liked me just because I have big feet."* My 93-year-old mother sighed. I remember the narrative so well that I imitated her voice and continued for her, *"The folks of the whole village came to see me, the bride. I was the only woman there without bound feet."* It worked, my mother grinned.

My mother was born in 1898 in a village about thirty *li* (miles) away from the village where Confucius was born, the center of rigid, ancient Chinese culture. Since about the 12th century, a dreadful custom had forced every little girl in China to have her feet bound at age five, so her feet would only grow to a size not longer than three Chinese inches (about 4 inches). The smaller a girl's feet were the better her chances to be considered beautiful, virtuous and able to wed a wealthy man. The poets and the artists termed the tiny feet "Golden Lilies." My mother did not have 'Golden Lilies' and she was ridiculed all her life.

Lately my aged mother has been quiet and withdrawn. Of course I knew the history of the foot binding well, but I wanted to hear my mother lecture me with her highly valued historical knowledge again. So I asked, *"Neon娘 (mother), when did the foot-binding start? The*

35

legendary female warrior, Mu-Lan, certainly had normal sized feet. If she had her feet bound, she could not be a soldier and the other soldiers would have known she was a woman immediately and not two years later when the war ended."

My mother chuckled, *"She invited her comrades to her home and served them tea in her maiden's clothes. Oh, they were surprised to know that Captain Hua Mu-lan was a woman."* After she sipped a little tea, she continued, *"Mu-lan's story is based on a very old poem written twelve hundred years ago during the Swei Dynast (600 A.D.). It was a story about a female warrior dressed as a man to fight a war in her aging father's place. It might not be a historical fact. About a thousand years ago, an emperor of the glorious Sung had a favorite concubine who had tiny feet. The legend had it that this petite court lady with tiny feet could dance on the leaves of the lotus. The Sung Emperor adored her so much that his other concubines all wore smaller, tighter shoes. Some of them even cut their feet with a knife to make them tiny. Ahe, we poor women would do anything to please men."* Mother sighed.

The custom of foot binding started in the royal palace, then the high-class society. When one Emperor of the Sung Dynasty (960 A.D.), himself an accomplished artist, praised the beauty of the tiny feet with poems and paintings, the terrible custom of foot binding became a set tradition all over China.

In the 17th century, the Manchu breached the Great Wall, conquered the Han 漢 (Chinese people) and established the Qing, or the Manchu Dynasty of China. The Manchu forced all the Chinese men to have the hair on the front of the head shaved off above the temples every ten days and the remainder of the hair was braided into a long braid-the Manchu queen. The hairstyle was compulsory for all males and the penalty for non-compliance was execution for treason. Many Chinese men refused and were killed. The Manchu were nomadic people and they needed their women's feet to grow naturally to walk, to ride and to fight.

My maternal grandpa favored all kinds of modern ideas on freedom and equality. He refused to have a concubine even though most of his friends, some of them of lower rank and comparatively not as wealthy, had one or more young concubines. He realized that the new era of man-woman equality, democracy and new technology from Germany and England would come to China soon. The more benevolent new ideology would certainly force China's old, unrealistic traditions out. Against his wife's bitter arguments, he insisted that his only daughter, my mother, must be spared the unspeakable suffering of foot binding and the life-long ordeal of walking on the deformed feet. In addition, he taught my mother to read and write so she would be prepared for the imminent culture changed new world. .

Looking down at her feet, my mother said, "*I remember very clearly that your grandpa was furious when he saw that my nanny pushed my feet into a pail of ice water to numb them before she could bind my feet with long strips of soaked cloth. He kicked the pail over, held me tight, slapped my nanny and yelled at my mother,*" My mother stopped talking and stared at nothing for a while and then continued with a cracked voice, "I *remember very well that your grandpa held me so tight and I yelled from fear. Before he put me down, his damp beard brushed my neck and I was shocked to think that my stern and formidable father actually was weeping. He died when I was ten years old, and my mother and me moved back to the country from Beijing.*" There was a forlorn look in my mother's old eyes and her wrinkled face seemed to have more lines. I suddenly remembered the dolls made of dried apples that I bought for my daughters in a country fair in Canada.

I lowered my head and blinked back the sudden moisture in my eyes. "*When was that? How old were you then?*" I asked somewhat hastily.

My mother replied, "*I was six years old. No, I was only five in the modern way to count the ages. At that time, we were one year old the day we were born. We were in Beijing. Your grandpa had a very good position. He was a magistrate of an important county. I remember that we lived in a big mansion with four courts.*"

"*Neon, it must have been very painful for a little girl to have her feet bound. Didn't my grandma love you? You were so little then, how could my grandma be so cruel to let you suffer?*"

37

"Every mother cried when they had to bind her daughter's feet. Sometimes a woman just could not do it herself; she would ask a friend to help. But, that was the custom. They had no choice. What could they do otherwise if they wanted their daughter to wed well? My mother complained to my father so often afterwards, she was worried that they could not find me a good husband from the upper class."

"The ruling Manchu women did not have bound-feet. They ruled China for more than two hundred years. How come the Emperors did not put a stop to foot binding?" I asked.

Mother said, *"I wish they had."*

The Manchu were the invaders. The Han, the local and original Chinese fought strongly against them. One city, the present day Yung Chou City, near Shanghai, put up a fierce and lengthy resistance. The Manchu eventually won and bloodied the city for ten whole days. After the Manchu conquered and controlled all of China in 1644, the local Chinese men did not want to shave their foreheads and braid their hair in the Manchu style. The Manchu killed so many of them. The resistance was widespread and continuous and the Manchu were afraid of a revolt if they forced the Chinese women to stop foot binding too.

I asked, *"Neon, I have never been to Beijing. Do you remember anything else when you were there?"*

"Not much. We had a big house and a lot of maids and servants. It's a long walk from our living quarter to the front gate. My mother, your grandma, had very tiny feet and was considered a beauty. She could not walk very well. Whenever my mother went out, maids supported her while she was walking and getting on and off the heavily draped sedan chair. Sometime she took me with her. We did not go out often. In the streets there were always some young students yelling and shouting for political and social changes. We had to have my father's soldiers to escort us."

"Neon", I asked again, *"Did the maids have their feet bound? If so, how could they work if they could not walk very well?"*

"Every woman had her feet bound, whether she was rich or poor. But the poor mostly did not bind their daughter's feet so

38

tightly and their feet were usually longer than the required three inches. Some of the working class women did have tiny feet, but they worked anyway. Some of them even knew martial arts and they could fight just like men did. I remember seeing one showgirl having tiny feet walking and dancing on a tight rope. At my home, my mother always let the maids and serving women have plenty of rest."

"Besides your nanny and maids, did you have friends to play with? What kind of games did you play?"

"Not many. I was the only daughter. Your two uncles were years older than me and they did not play with me. Besides, they had a tutor and they also went to school. Two little girls about my age that I knew sat all the time and often cried. You see, they both just had their feet bound and their feet hurt a lot. When they saw me jump and run, they cried harder." Mother continued, *"Later my mother taught me embroidery when my father was at work. Your grandfather often said something like this to your grandmother, "Don't you know the world is changing? It's not necessary to know how to do embroidery now. My baby has to know how to read and write first so that later she can learn anything new by herself. Forget about teaching her embroidery now. She only needs to know how to do some simple sewing. Soon there will be sewing machines in China too.""* Mother continued, *"After I was seven years old, sometimes your grandpa would hold my hand to teach me how to write. Guess what? When I was eight years old, my father ordered that I be dressed like a boy so I could go to the tutor's classroom in the frontcourt. The maids used to call me jokingly 'Third young master' then."* My mother sighed and continued, *"My father would have sent me to a school if he had not died so soon."*

At the time when my mother was young, the Qing, the Manchu Dynasty weakened. Dr. Sun Yat-sen, the founding father of the Republic of China led a revolutionary movement to overthrow the Manchu Emperor and to eradicate the old customs of slavery and foot binding. There were many student demonstrations in the bigger cities. Unfortunately, my grandpa was wounded and died during one of the revolts and left my mother without an arranged mate as the custom dictated.

Traditionally, the well-to-do families arranged their youngsters' marriages between themselves when the children were quite young. No decent family wanted to have my mother, a girl with big feet, full of modern ideas, to be their son's mate. At twenty-one without a promised marriage, my mother became a bona-fide old maid.

I put the slippers on my mother's feet and tied the strips. The slippers fit all right and they were very becoming. I murmured, "*Too bad that the socks are blue, I should have bought a pair of pink ones.*" Looking down at her slippers, my mother said, "*You know the family of Confucius lived not far away from my home. One day, some women from the Confucius family came to my home. They looked over the girls about my age to choose a wife for their son. As soon as they saw my big feet, they chose my fat cousin who had a big flat nose and small pox scars, instead. Even though everyone could see that I was the prettiest one with a nice complexion.*" Her eyes flashed momentarily with anger. It seemed to me that my aged mother had not forgotten the rejection from almost a century ago.

I forced a laugh and said, "*Lucky for me,* my *father came along.*" I knew that the marriage was not a happy one. My mother was highly versed in history and classical Chinese literature, but my father did not have a good foundation of the Chinese language and literature. He was one of the impoverished boys who received a grant from the government of the newly founded Republic of China to be educated in Japan when he was only 14 years old. So, it was a bad match: old-fashioned versus new and modern, wealth versus poverty. My father died at the age of 70 in 1967 in Taiwan.

My parents' marriage was arranged. Through the countryside grapevine, one of my mother's cousins heard that my father, the fourth son of a poor family of nine sons, was in need of a wife with a rich dowry. Of course, my father had no prejudicial ideas against big feet. As a matter of fact, he considered bound feet old-fashioned. At that time the government had already enforced the "feet-free" movement first in big cities like Shanghai and Beijing.

My mother received a photo of my father showing a tall, handsome young student. As for my mother, she could not have a photograph taken of her because there were no photographers in the village. Besides, country folk were superstitious. They believed that the flash of the camera could steal the soul. My grandma hired a professional painter to do a portrait of my pretty, petite mother. So, a marriage contract was finalized, and that's how my mother with her big feet finally got married.

As I helped my mother to her bedroom, I thought, "Whenever a social custom changes, someone is victimized. Regardless if the change is from good to bad or vice-versa. My mother just happened to live through one of these changes, and she carried the irreversible sorrow all her life. She had been ridiculed because she did not have her feet bound. As a result of having normal size feet, she could not marry into the distinguished family of Confucius and instead married a poor student. It must have been quite a letdown, and a bitter pill for her to swallow. In a way, my mother's feet, and her fate, had been bound, not by strips of cotton, but by a form of 'human bondage'."

-End-

Note: My mother came to live with me in Pueblo, Colorado in 1991. She passed away in 1998.

First Wife

The first snow of 1986 threatened St. Louis with low clouds and frost. Mai-ann 美安 shivered and pulled her raincoat tighter around her when she got off the bus in front of "Sunset Garden," an apartment complex for senior citizens. She carried her purse over her left shoulder and held the heavy shopping bag of Chinese food with her left arm, groaning softly from the dull ache of her arthritic right shoulder. As usual, she bought a bit more than she could easily carry, but she could not resist buying the fresh shrimp and leeks that were on sale. With these, she could cook her husband Gee-fu 紀夫 a special treat.

"I hope there was no letter from Mainland China again," she murmured to herself after finding no mail. Gee-fu 紀夫 always waited anxiously to get the mail from China. She would be very upset if Gee-fu, who was suffering from a bad cold, had picked up the mail while she was shopping. *"He may hide it. He does not want me to know."*

Holding a letter from his oldest son in Mainland China, Gee-fu was startled, "Why didn't you call me down to help you?" Mai-ann 美安 thought unhappily, *"What's the use. You can't help me."* Instead she asked, "Another letter from your son? What does your family want this time?" She nearly spat out the words 'your family.'

Gee-fu lowered his head, avoiding her look of accussation and whispered, "They want me back China. She is quite ill." He then hastily raised his voice, "Just for a visit." Mai-ann wanted to shout, *"Go back to them then. Let her take her turn to look after you. What do I care? After I divorce you, I'm still young enough to marry someone who may be younger than you! We'll see, won't we?"* Instead, she dropped the grocery bag on the kitchen counter with a bang and went into the bathroom. She sighed and now she was angry with herself for being bitter and suspicious. She was displeased with herself for feeling self-pity. Most of all, she was angry about being forced to face a hopeless situation which none of them could alter. With a comb in her left hand, she combed her windblown hair hard enough to hurt her scalp. She looked at her anguished and angered face in the mirror. There were dark rings under her once youthful, pretty, big eyes. The hateful smallpox scars showed clearly. *"We've been married for thirty-three years"* she thought, *'I do not deserve to be treated like this. Why can't you forget her? Or could I forget her? Of course, none of us could wipe out the fact that she exists anyway. I want your full attention!'* Her *conflicting* thoughts darted this way and that way just like her hairs - long, short, with split ends, straight and curved.

Mai-ann was twenty-eight years old when she married forty-two year old Gee-fu in Taiwan. When she consulted her parents about the marriage, her mother opposed, "He is too old for you, and he must have a wife back home." Man-ann said, "Yes, he does and he has a son. He told me." Her usually quiet father said, "At least he is honest. I don't think that he will see his family again." It had been seven years since Chiang Kai-shek's Nationalist Chinese government had been defeated and withdrawn from Mainland China in 1949. All the people who disagreed with and were frightened of the Communists followed him to Taiwan. During and after the total chaos of the Chinese civil war between the Nationalists and the Communists from 1945 to 1949, many families were separated, properties and savings lost.

In 1956, Gee-fu was an instructor of Chinese classics at a community college not far away from where Mai-ann was an elementary school teacher at Keelung, Taiwan. He visited Mai-ann and her roommate often and enjoyed a home-cooked meal once in a while. He was attracted to Mai-ann.'s straightforward manners and to the deep sense of caring and filial devotion she had for her parents and younger siblings. Mai-ann found that she could tell Gee-fu just about anything. Mai-ann also often asked Gee-fu for his advice on teaching and classroom management. He would tell her how much he missed and worried about his wife and son who had been left behind when he escaped to Taiwan. More and more married men who had wives back in Mainland China would marry again. Both the government and the general public agreed that this act of double marriage was a regrettable but unavoidable necessity. Traditionally, every Chinese male should have at least one child, preferably a boy, to carry on the family name and bloodline. Remaining unmarried without the assurance of at least one surviving offspring would be considered an act of default of family consciousness and responsibility.

Gee-fu proposed, "You know that I was married before but I have little hope of seeing my wife and my son again. I'll love you and cherish you as much as I can if you are willing to be my wife. You know that I'm much older than you." Mai-ann was truly surprised when he asked her to marry him. Her height and her big bones made her look stout and she always had been self-conscious about her smallpox scars on her face. For a long time, she thought that Gee-fu's frequent visits were to court her pretty and petite roommate.

They had three children, two sons and a daughter. When their first son was born, Gee-fu said, "The word for this precious boy's generation is "Shih 士 (Scholar)". Shih-ming (bright, wisdom) 士明 is the name I have chosen for my son back home in Mainland China. We will call this boy Shih-yen士仁 (kindness). If Lo *tin yeh* (the supreme God) grants them the opportunity to meet in the future, they will know that they are brothers." He named their second son Shih-yun 士勇 (bravery) and their daughter Shih-hua 士華 (graceful). Gee-fu never had a strong constitution. Frequent escapes from Communist pursuers in his 30's weakened him more. The responsibilities of a young family and many late nights of writing and editing of Chinese Classics textbooks took a heavy toll on his health. He contracted tuberculosis. Twice he had been seriously ill and Mai-ann was very afraid. She shouldered everything - teaching, keeping the house, and nursing her sick husband - with unbending loyalty and fortitude. Eventually, Gee-fu recovered. A few books he wrote were published and gained public recognition.

44

Mai-ann and her husband came to the United States to be close to their children and grandchildren. They were at peace and content with their lives until Communist China opened their doors to the West. News came that Gee-fu's first wife in Mainland China had survived the civil war and the chaos of the Cultural Revolution in the 70's.

Deep in her confused reverie, Mai-Ann dropped the face-cream jar; it hit the spotless tiled floor and shattered into pieces. "*Just like my life, shattered and in pieces*," she murmured. Gee-fu asked anxiously, "Did you hurt yourself? Did you break something?"

"Don't worry. I just dropped the face-cream jar." She cleaned up the mess.

In the living room, she found Gee-fu napping on the recliner. Looking at his sallow complexion full of age spots, Mai-ann.'s heart ached. Her eyes swam with tears and she pulled her hand-knitted lap blanket up to his chin.

She started to prepare the meal in the kitchen. She was wondering, not for the first time, about her latest decision. Lately, Mai-ann spent many sleepless nights considering her dilemma. She couldn't help feeling sorry for Gee-fu's first wife, as only a Chinese woman could comprehend. She understood what a miserable existence the other woman must have lived all the years, without a husband, under harsh Communist control. Many times she told herself, '*It's nobody's fault that we, the three of us, and many other Chinese who share the same predicament were all victims of a historical disaster beyond our control.*' Her natural kind nature gradually overcame her initial feelings of jealousy and anger.

A few days ago, she phoned her younger sister, Mai-ling, and told her that she agreed that Gee-fu should go to China to visit his first wife "But I wish that he would come back to me, She sobbed, "What would I do if he wants to stay there with her? I just cannot live without him."

"Why shouldn't he come back?" her sister asked, "He loves you. Everybody knows that. You are a kind and wonderful wife, mother, sister and teacher. Remember that you always tell me that one should have more confidence. You're scared because you love him too much. He'll come back to you and he will love you even more for your kindness and generosity. Honestly, I don't think he can live without you."

The soup was simmering; the ingredients washed, cut, marinated, and ready to cook. The phone rang. Gee-fu woke up.

"Wei (hello) Mai-ling, my baby sister," she answered," How are you?"

She listened to Mai-ling, paused, and responded, "Thanks, but I think it will be easy for Shih-yun士勇to take some time off to go with him.... I know you'd like to help. …. He is getting better every day, and I hope he can take it…. I'll tell him you said hello. Take care and bye."

"Mai-ling thinks you're her mother, not her sister," said Gee-fu, "You actually brought her up and she is grateful. But, what were you talking about? Why does Shih-yun have to take time off? For what? Going where?"

"It's a secret," she replied. "Get well quick and then I'll tell you." Somehow, her voice quivered a little. She did not want Gee-fu to see her face, so she turned around to look at the family portrait on the wall beside the bookshelves.

She wiped her hands again, making sure that they were very clean. Then Mai-ann proudly touched the neatly displayed books that Gee-fu wrote. '*I know you're the best husband a plain woman like me could ever hope to have,*' she thought, '*We've been through a lot. We have prayed together and laughed together. I just cannot live without you. I cannot bear a separation, even a short one. But, I know you must have loved her too. I have had your company and love for more than thirty years now. And it will be fair at least to let her have her chance. She is older than I am and she is sick. It is not easy for me to let you go and I pray that you will come back to me.*" Her hot tears came, her back slumped and her shoulders trembled. Gee-fu walked to her and held her silently; their tears mingled. Outside, the wind stopped and the autumn sun shone on a few green leaves left on the tree.

-End-

46

Note: The first version –title "My husband's other wife in Communist China" was published in 1990. Pen and Palette. The creative arts journal of the University of Southern Colorado, Issue Number 2, Spring 1990

A snowy night in Canada

'*W*hy did I marry your father?' I wanted to write something about myself to my young daughters, and after a few unsatisfactory beginnings, I finally decided to start with questions and answers.

'*Because I was so unhappy with my family situation. Also, I was twenty-six years old and held a humdrum job that did not pay very much at that time.*' In 1966, all the other young people were trying to leave the overcrowded Taiwan for the United States. I got a small scholarship and tried to leave but I did not have enough money for the trip. '*You see, your father was assigned to be a medical doctor abroad and I thought naively that a marriage was my only way 'OUT'.*'

I paused and stared at the few typed lines, and suddenly and realized the quiet of the night had become unbearable. Wee-fan 惟方and Wee-hua's 惟華soft breathing reminded me anew of the harsh responsibility of raising them alone, six thousand miles away from home. The same home I'd tried to leave.

I went to the two side-by-side used cribs to check on the girls again; halfway there, I turned and walked to the window to look out into the snowy night through my tears. The wide street, blanketed with deep snow, was lined with tall leafless trees and bungalows with front yards, and driveways with snow topped cars. There were spaces everywhere: between and in front of the houses, between the sidewalk and the wide street. A car drove slowly by and the huge snow hauling truck was just turning around the corner. Everywhere I looked, I saw the obvious differences between here and the crowded suburb of Taipei, Taiwan. Space and the piled snow made me keenly

48

aware of my loneliness in London, Canada. My longing for the crowded Taiwan almost became tangible.

Mechanically, I wiped my persistent tears and watched the floating snowflakes, which, just like my thoughts, scattered in all directions. Against the vast emptiness, I wanted to shout, *'Wee-fan and Wee-hua, someday when you read this, you might understand why your mother so easily became cross with you, even when you did nothing wrong. Right now I feel trapped.'* You two are too young for us to start fresh in Washington D.C. or New York City with my bilingual skills. Instead, we must live on the shameful "Mothers' Allowance". We're lucky that the Canadian government looks after single mothers. *'Oh! It's so hard to swallow the humiliation of living on welfare, but what can I do when you girls are only two and three years old?'* The traces of memory were as numerous as the strands of my abundant long black hair. Some strands of my hair were straight and shining, others were curved. There were even a few split ends. I guess I could cut off the split ends, just like how I would automatically try to cut short my bad memories. I try not to think about the unhappy recollections by burying them deep inside of me. But, I must tell my girls the truth and I must face the past with its mix of pleasant, painful, and even ugly moments.

In 1966, I graduated with a bachelor's degree from Chengchi University in Taipei, Taiwan. After I taught two years at a high school, I jumped hastily into a bad marriage.

'"Why?" I can hear you asking me.'

'Oh, well I'm ashamed to tell you the truth. I was 26 years old and I didn't have a steady boyfriend and I desperately wanted to escape from a rotten family situation.' Your grandparents couldn't get along with each other. They quarreled often.

I did not go through the normal schooling--junior high, senior high and university. When I grew up, only the elementary school education was free in Taiwan. One had to pay tuition and fees to attend junior or senior high. Your grandpa simply did not make enough money to educate your youngest aunt, two uncles and me. Of course, since I'm the youngest one and a girl, the family's purse would pay for my two brothers' tuitions first. So, I attended an

"Elementary School Teachers Training School" after junior high with other impoverished girls of my age. There was an urgent demand for elementary school teachers since thousands and thousands people escaped to Taiwan from mainland China in 1949. The students attending this expressed teachers' training school would receive a monthly stipend, free room and food, uniforms and books, and even socks and shoes for three years. Each student would receive a teacher's certificate upon graduation and must be, required by law, an elementary school teacher for three years.

Some of my long hairs tangled with the keys of the old fashioned portable Underwood typewriter. While untangling my hair, I murmured to myself, '*I had no choice.*' Even at fifteen, I had hoped to be independent and leave home early. I could walk to school but I chose to live in the dormitory to get away from your grandma's constant complaints and whining of being poor after the affluent lifestyle she was used to in North China. I also could not stand your grandpa's cold and silent indifference. The decision to attend the 'Elementary School Teachers Training School' was forced on me. There was no alternative and I had no freedom to choose anyway.

I stood up and stretched while looking at the shabby furniture and the faded curtains of the cheaply furnished apartment. I wanted to shout, '*Oh! How I did dream about having a perfect marriage and the best education for my children! But now...*"

I had a wonderful dream for my future. The compositions I wrote for my junior high school's writing class always earned me high praises. It made me want to become a writer someday. I really wanted to earn a college degree.

But your grandpa said, "Mai-ling, you should go to the government paid teachers' training school and you'll be able to support yourself right away. I'm almost sixty years old and I really do not have the means to pay for you to attend high school and then university. I know your grades are good and you have earned some monetary rewards. They are not enough. Although your second elder brother is enrolled in a free military college now, I still have to pay for your third brother's college tuition. You must know that there is a big increase in the high school tuition this fall again. Besides, I do think that teaching would be a good position for an ordinary and homely girl like you." I wanted to plead and tell your grandpa my dream, but I dared not to and he resumed reading immediately anyway.

I remember that I cried on the bus all the way to register at the 'Elementary School Teachers Training School'. The privilege of enrolling at the most prestigious high school, which I earned through a tough entrance examination, was lost to me forever. My tears drenched my faded black skirt and quite a few passengers on the bus gawked at me.

"Girl! What's the matter? Has something awful happened?" A kind woman put her arms around me and asked. I shook my head. I did not wear a white ribbon in my hair and a white armband, and she knew that there was no death in my family.

The keyboard caught the splash of my huge teardrops and I pulled out the dampened paper. The wailing violin on the radio filled the emptiness of the chilled room and tore my heart apart. I turned it off.

The courses that the 'Elementary School Teachers Training School' offered concentrated on the Chinese language, history and simple arithmetic and basic teaching techniques. There were no Algebra and English classes. I graduated ranking the 5th out of three hundred students and fulfilled my obligation as an elementary school teacher for three years.

Feeling the quiet of the night closing in on me, I laughed aloud, *'Guess what! I was almost eighteen when an inspector from the Department of Education mistook me for a student and scolded me for wandering in the hall and not wearing the student uniform.'*

The scenario made me grin. I was five feet and two inches tall, and slender with a round face that made me look younger. My short hair was styled like a student since I did not have the money for a perm and a stylish hair cut. One day when I was walking along the hallway, a man yelled at me, "You! Stop right there! Why are you not in class? Why are you not wearing a uniform?"

I was startled and stammered, "I... I'm a teacher." Then, recovering, I asked him with dignity and authority, "Who are you? Parents are not supposed to be in the hallway. I'll take you to the office...." By that time, the principal walked up and began the introductions, "Mr. Yong is an inspector, and Miss Lee is one of our brilliant new teachers." The inspector laughed and I blushed.

I enjoyed teaching, but I secretly envied my classmates from junior high. They were university students by then. The spirit of competition and wanting more made me study English and Algebra after work. I passed the highly competitive college entrance examination, and was accepted by the prestigious Chengchi University. I even won a four-year full paid scholarship from the Highway Bureau where your grandpa was a senior engineer. I had to study really hard, though, to fill the gap of my interrupted academic education. Also I was three years older than my classmates, and I often felt out-of-place. My teaching experiences and maturity made it hard for me to be carefree like the others. Besides, my lack of three years of English lessons caused difficulties and made me feel inferior and it was difficult to find a boyfriend then.

There was a very brief romantic encounter. I met a scholarly, sophisticated man in his forties. We enjoyed talking about books and poetry, and I felt close to him. To me, he was a father figure rather than a boyfriend. Your grandma strongly advised against the courtship and I withdrew sullenly but obediently.

Jobs were scarce in Taiwan with so many university graduates. I applied for and received a small grant for a graduate school program from a university in Iowa, United States. But, I did not have enough money saved for the trip even if I worked part-time to supplement the scanty scholarship. Also, at that time my family situation worsened. Your grandparents, both in the sixties, finally separated. Divorce or separation was so unusual in such a strongly family-oriented society in Taiwan at that time. You could imagine that I was very embarrassed. I hesitated to take part in any social events and was afraid of being asked to go to a family dinner since I knew that I could never invite anyone to my home.

I got a position to teach English at a senior high school in another town sixty miles away, and commuted by train daily. I still enjoyed teaching, but the pay was low. My busy schedule and the unpleasant family setting made me evade meeting any suitable young man. Many of my classmates and other university graduates were either studying abroad or preparing to go to the States or Europe. By then most of my girlfriends from the teachers' training school were married with children.

Recalling my predicament, I remembered that I often thought that my youth and ambition were being wheeled away bit by bit along with the monotonous moving wheels of the train that I had to ride daily to work. I wanted then to be married soon. *"Girls, when you are older, you will understand that no young woman wants to be an old maid.'*

'How did I meet your father?' One day you will ask me.

And I'll tell you, *'Well, he was the doctor who surgically removed my infected fingernail.'*

I am the youngest child of seven. When I was born, your grandma was forty-one years old and did not get along with your grandpa. Often, your grandma told me that I was an unwanted girl. I was often sick and do not have good coordination, so I fell easily and I am prone to minor accidents. One winter, I split the fingernail on the middle finger of my right hand. Holding the chalk everyday made it difficult for the nail to heal. It got infected. I had to go to the hospital, and your father was the attending doctor.

Outside the wind roared, and the snow slashed hard against the window. I felt the temperature dropping, so I checked on the sleeping girls and covered them and then sat staring at the typewriter.

Your father, a good doctor, was actually very attentive when he treated my infected finger. He told me that soon he would be leaving Taiwan for a position as a physician in Libya, Africa.

I whispered almost in a pleading tone, *'Girls! You have to understand, at that time I thought that getting married might be my only way 'OUT'...out of my miserable home to a new life abroad.'*

After the marriage, we went to Libya. Pretty soon I realized that I made a terrible mistake since it was not a marriage of love but rather a marriage of convenience. I wanted to have a home of my own and your father married me for my good education, especially, for my knowledge of the English language. Also, your father slightly resembled the other man I had met before. I really didn't know your father well and gradually I found out there were many differences in our social backgrounds, upbringing, manners, tastes, and political views.

I frowned and sighed when I vividly recalled the irritating sound of my ex-husband smacking his lips at meals. Bound by culture and tradition, and being so far away from home, I did not dare to divorce him. Besides, I was pregnant with Wee-fan.

Striving to be fair, I sighed, *'Girls, I don't want you to think that your father was a bad man. As a matter of fact, he was brilliant in his profession and a very good father. He loved me in his own way and tried to be a good husband, but...'*

I shivered, not from the cold but from the bitter memory, when I thought of the endless political arguments with your father. He was pro-Communist and always secretly wanted to go back to Communist China (Mainland China), even though he worked and was educated in Taiwan since 1949. The Chinese Communist Party, who confiscated my family's real estate holdings in Northern China, had prosecuted my family. My whole family had to escape to Taiwan in 1949. Of course I was, and still am, against Communism and would not consider going back to live under the Communist regime.

We did not go back to Taiwan after your father's contract in Libya ended, and came to Canada instead. In the 60's, Canada was one of the few countries that recognized Communist China, not the Nationalist Taiwan, as the official Chinese government. There was a Chinese embassy (not of Taiwan) in Ottawa. Your father wanted to take the both of you and me back to Communist China. I refused to go and he became violent. After we separated, I had to raise you girls alone.

Staring at the tear-stained typed pages, I involuntarily shook more out of loneliness than the cold. So I called aloud, *'It's late and I'm so tired of struggling with English. Someday, I will write it more clearly, so you can read it.'* Lying awake on a cot between the two cribs, my hot tears rolled.

The first ray of dawn filtered through the shabby curtains. With an effort, I opened my swollen eyelids and walked toward the window. Bright morning rays shone on the black tree trunks contrasting with the cotton-like piles of snow on the dropping branches. It was so beautiful. Marveling at the serene beauty, my spirit suddenly lifted. I knew then that I must be strong, for my own sake as well as for my daughters. The crystal clear peaceful dawn after a stormy night symbolized a new beginning.

-End-

Ha-en海安 & Shu-hua 書華

Water was at a premium at San Jose, California in 1994. Shu-hua書華 adjusted the kitchen faucet to let the water trickle down in a thin line. She washed the celery and spinach one leaf at a time, with her back slightly stooped, shifting her weight from one foot to the other. A Beijing opera was on the TV in the living room and her husband, Ha-en海安 was singing along with it. She depressed a sigh and somehow her eyes moistened. Either out of longtime repressed discontentment or from a nagging worry, she could not tell.

Sensing the sigh rather than hearing it, Ha-en海安 came into the kitchenette.

"For goodness' sake, you need not wash them one leaf at a time. Here they don't fertilize the vegetables with human waste like they used to do in Taiwan. Besides, the famers cleaned it pretty good before selling it in the supermarket." He said.

"But, there's fine sand on the leaves. John told me that the spray the farmers used on it is not exactly healthy either. You have a weak stomach." Shu-hau replied and she regretted immediately that she had mentioned their 2nd son's opinion. She thought, 'Oh No. He will order me to go to John's house again. Oh. Lo Tien Jia 老天爺 (God of the sky) please helps me. Does he finally want to get rid of me? Have I not been an obedient wife all these years?'

"I bet he did. Of course, the smart ass should know. By the way, his baby will be born soon and we have to buy your plane tickets now. It will be cheaper." Ha-en海安 said.

"I...I...I'm not sure that I want to go to Phoenix without you. Who will look after you?" Shu-hua 書華 said. She really wanted to

56

ask him why he does not want to go with her, but his stern expression stopped her. For years now, he hardly ever raised his voice at her, but she knew better.

"Don't be silly. I know how to cook. Besides, I can eat all my meals at Jason's restaurant. No need to worry, I won't starve. How can the father of a restaurant owner starve? " Ha-en said.

"I…I cannot talk with our American-born Chinese daughter-in-law. She can hardly speak Cantonese and she does not speak a word of Mandarin. You know that I can only speak a few English words but you speak English well. Please don't send me there alone." Shu-hua whined.

"With my pidgin English? The simple English I learned on the ship is by far not up to her class." John's wife was raised by her German-American step-father. She and her brother cannot speak Chinese. Ha-en continued, "She is Chinese outside and American inside. She looks like a typical Chinese girl but she is not a Chinese girl anymore. There are so many pretty Chinese students from Taiwan, Shanghai and Beijing; John could have a good picking with his good looks. But, instead, he married one who can't speak Chinese. Later, we cannot even talk with our grandkids." He complained.

"But…" Her voice was so thin. It seems that she was her usual silent self again. Actually, what Shu-hua wanted to say was that John had married for love. She loves to read romance novels. She thought, '*what's the use of talking to him about love. He won't understand. His idea of a wife is someone who cleans the house, raises the children and is totally obedient. The wife should stay home when he goes out to get drunk or have some fun, and then clean him up when he comes back drunk. That's all. If he knows or feels a little bit of love, it would be different.*'

What would be different? She was not quite clear. She shuddered at her memories of the beating she got from him when they were newly married. Ha-en would shut her up with fists when she still had the courage to have her opinions and wishes known. Once she fell when she tried to run away from him and nearly lost her first son to a miscarriage. The beating stopped afterwards, but not his dominance. However, Shu-hua became totally obedient ever since she was pregnant with her second son. She no longer gave her suggestions and opinions on any matter, big or small, even when she knew she was right.

There were so many people from different provinces in mainland China who escaped from Communist China to Taiwan, so jobs were scarce. Shu-hua found an elementary teaching job at Hualian, a port on the east coast of Taiwan, and far away from her home in Taipei. Her height and her large frame make her appear awkward. She has always been self-conscious about the small-pox scars on her face, even though she has a nice complexion and beautiful big eyes. She was twenty-eight years old when she married thirty-seven-year-old Ha-en in 1956. It had been seven years after the free Nationalist Chinese government had withdrawn from Communist-occupied mainland China, and the general public finally admitted that it was an impossible dream to fight against Mao tse-tung's huge army, and to claim back the lost homeland. They all knew that if the Seventh Fleet of the United States had not guarded the Taiwan Strait in 1949, Mao's Communist Army would have seized Taiwan, too. Many husbands who had escaped to Taiwan alone were married again. Shu-hua's parents did not want her to marry someone who had a family before. Ha-en told them that he had been a sailor ever since he was 15 and had no wife. They let Shu-hua 書華 marry him even though Ha-en海安, a short Cantonese, was half an inch shorter than Shu-hua. They hoped that their new son-in-law, being a sailor, would help Shu-hua's younger siblings to go to the United States. It was Shu-hua's elder sister, a medical doctor, and her brother, a prominent architect, who sponsored Ha-en's family to the United States twenty-two years ago.

They had struggled through the first ten years after they came to San Jose, CA. At first, they did not have their own home; Shu-hua 書華 was a live-in babysitter and housemaid. Ha-en海安 slept on a cot in the restaurant where he washed dishes and cleaned the tables. Their two sons stayed with Shu-hua's brother in Arizona. Then they lived in an apartment shared with two families. Luck was with them when the first mate, now retired, of the ocean liner that Ha-en was a sailor on, ate at the restaurant where Ha-en worked.

This man helped them both to be hired by, and work for, an old wealthy American couple. Ha-en did the shopping, and kept the yard, and Shu-hua was a housemaid. Ha-en learned some simple American cooking when he was a sailor and he gradually took over the cooking from the old lady. Both of them were loyal and worked hard. Their employers liked them and their sons, and let the family live in a little cottage. Five years ago, the old woman passed away. Their daughter took the old man to Ohio, sold the big house with the stipulation that Ha-en and his wife could live in the cottage for life with a $100.00 monthly rent. They fixed it up and it's a nice home.

Both of them quit working full-time now. They pulled their savings together to help Jason, their first born, to own a restaurant, and John, the second son, a professor in Arizona. They were supposed to be happy, but were they? Shu-hua was glad that Ha-en treated her better and even with some genuine respect. The gentle ways their employers treated each other had been a good influence on Ha-en. But Shu-hua felt uneasy whenever her husband looked at her with a sorrowful and sympathetic expression in his eyes. It almost seemed that he wants to leave her. She wondered and asked herself, '*Did he know? Had he keep silent all these years?*' She wondered and she dared not to ask.

Ha-en海安

It was a Beijing opera on the TV. Ha-en would prefer a Cantonese opera, but he sang along with the actor anyway. His mind switched between the show and his wife when the sound of Shu-hua's moving around and the rattling of something, probably the pot and dishes, came through the hanging divider between the living area and the kitchenette. Ha-en海安 sighed and asked himself the same question again, '*We made it, but why can't we be happy?*' He acutely felt her melancholy as heavy as his own. He loves her, and he knows that he owes his solid, steadfast wife a lot. Somehow he could not breach the wall between them. He sighed, '*This impregnable wall between us has been getting as thick as the Great Wall and as wide as the Yangzi River over the years. I'm not even sure when it started. Did it start before or after that…Does she know that I have known.*

I am the one to blame.' He truly regretted that he started to abuse her physically shortly after they were wed. *'That was the root of it. I had pushed her into it.'*

He recalled that he was actually slightly afraid of her being taller than him, and he had also noticed that his dominate mother-in-law ordered his father-in-law around. So he decided he had to take the traditional role of a domineering husband and showed her that he's the boss. He grew up watching his father beat his mother left and right, and the fathers of his friends all behaved the same way toward their wives. Most parents beat their children, too. That was the normal way his parents' generation lived by. Ha-en海安 did not have the opportunity to know that it was wrong. He left home to work on ships with rough seamen ever since he was only a boy. He was drunk often and he fought fiercely, but he had never touched any woman whenever he was onshore. He kept his responsibility to his family. His great grandpa was an only child and so was his grandpa, his father and him. His family was desperately in need of more children, especially sons. Ha-en's father and his grandma abused his mother because she did not have more children after Ha-en. His father bought a concubine who did not have any children either, but her presence and her unruly manners caused Ha-en's grandma and his mother's death. One of his grandma's death wishes was that Ha-en would marry a strong and tall northern Chinese girl to have strong children. Ha-en recalled that not once his grandma had repeated, "Ha-en, don't marry a short local Cantonese girl. Find a wife from Northern China, we need new blood". He chuckled, *'Grandma would have approved of Shu-hua. It is my fault that I only have two sons. Two or one?'*

Ha-en was 15 years old in 1935. His maternal uncle, who was an engineer on an American Pacific liner, came back for his sister's funeral. His uncle did not want Ha-en to be abused by the stepmother so he told Ha-en's father, "The aggressive Japanese armies have occupied part of northern China already. They want to conquer China completely and an all-out war between China and Japan is imminent. Let me take Ha-en to America." The older village boys were forced to join the army. So his father agreed and told Ha-en,

60

"Remember what your grandma had told you. Don't learn any bad habits from the sailors. Keep yourself clean and stay away from bad women. Marry a strong woman to have strong children. It's your responsibility to the family." The eight-year Sino-Japanese war erupted in 1937 when the Japanese attacked the Marco Polo Bridge adjacent to Beijing. In 1941, World War II began and ended in 1945. Then the civil war between the Chinese Nationalist and Chinese Communists started. Ha-en has not been back to his hometown in Guangdong, China since he left home in 1935.

The actor on the TV sang that he wanted to go home to his wife. Ha-en thought, '*So do I. I want to go home, too.*' Many Chinese of his generation has never considered Taiwan or U.S. as their 'home'. When they talk about 'going home', they mean their hometown or village in China where they were born and raised. A persistent and ever present image of a young girl with cleft lip and crystal clear eyes came to Ha-en, '*I want to go home to her. Now I know that Li-jei*李姐 *is part of the wall between me and my wife.*" Ha-en sighed.

At the airport

Shu-hua walked behind Ha-en and Jason who carried her small suitcase. She never had many clothes. She noticed that Jason was a slightly taller, younger version of his father, with the same narrow shoulders and short legs. They were even walking with the same gait. She thought, '*John, my baby boy is tall and handsome. He sure looks different.*' Somehow, she tried to suppress a knowing smile.

They were sending her off to Phoenix. She missed John and she was glad that she would see him soon. But she also did not want to go alone and there was a lingering tight knot of suspicion in her mind that Ha-en海安 deliberately wanted to send her away so he could do something. '*What could it be?*' She did not know. But she has a premonition that something will happen. Ha-en explained to her that there are two reasons why he does not want to accompany her.

Ha-en told her, "Shu-hua 書華, you should know that John and I are not always on the same circuit. I'm afraid that I may lose my temper, or argue with him, in front of our daughter-in-law. I don't want to lose face."

She had argued, "She does not understand Cantonese very well."

Ha-en said, "Come on. She can read our facial expressions and the tone of our voices. Besides, the Chinese Mid-Autumn Festival 中秋節is here, I have to help Jason in the restaurant. You will be back in a month or so, and you can always use the money that I gave you to come back sooner if you're not happy there."

Shu-hua felt out the $2000 dollars, in twenty $100 bills, hidden in a zippered secret pocket inside the waist of the pair of long pants she wore. It felt good. Ha-en had been extra nice to her the last two weeks. When he gave her the money, he said, "You should have enough money of your own and you don't have to ask our daughter-in-law for money if you want to buy something for the baby or for yourself. I know you will live for even less. You will not ask her for money. It's warmer there in Arizona. Ask John to take you shopping and buy yourself some new clothes before the baby is born. I don't want you to feel embarrassed that you don't have some nice clothes to wear. Besides, you need to have some money to come back anytime you want if you are not happy there.' She almost cried from his kind words at that time, and now she is wondering whether he is sorry and if the money is compensation for the pain that she will suffer when he did what he has planned to do. She wondered and comforted herself with a thought, '*Would I really be sad if he were leaving? None of us are happy anyway. Actually it would not be too bad to be alone if he wants to leave me. I would enjoy the freedom.*'

Jason, the first son

Jason drove his father home. His father kept on talking about inconsequential things. But somehow Jason sensed his father's sadness. '*No, it's not sadness. Remorse? Relief? Maybe uneasiness?*'

He does resemble his father a lot, but he also has his mother's sensibilities. He had cried hours when the family cat died, run over by a truck, when he was fifteen, so he was known for being sentimental. Lately, whenever he could, he would sit with his usually silent mother for a long time. He knows that she likes it very much. Ever since he was a child, he was aware that something was not quite right between his parents. Both of them are talkative with their friends, but not with each other. They are cheerful when there are others around. Whenever they are alone, his father always criticizes and verbally abuses his mother who would always keep quiet. His mother has always been afraid of his father and she is very obedient. He knows that his mother loves him and John equally, but he is not quite sure about his father who obviously prefers him to his younger brother. '*Why?*' He could never figure out and it was painful to see the way his father ignored his brother. John towers over him by more than a head, and is very handsome and smart. His mother always told others that John gets the looks from her family. Indeed, Jason's three maternal uncles are tall, but John has finer features. '*I was so jealous of John's good looks and academic achievements; even I love him with my whole heart.*' He recalled the embarrassment he felt when he was with his tall, younger brother. '*He is 18 months younger than me. Yet some folks thought that I was the younger one.*' He always felt so uncomfortable at home when both his parents behaved like they were strangers. Because of this, he vows that he will be completely open with his wife.

Since last summer, an elder Chinese man came to visit his father at the restaurant often. They talked with a different dialect, which he could not understand well. His father and this man would talk and talk for a long time and his father would look both sad and happy after each visit. He always wondered '*why?*', but his Chinese upbringing forbids him to ask his father. His parents have not been happy together for a long time, and he almost feels that any change might do them both good. Jason told his wife his concerns. Anna said, "It's time that they do something about it. They are so unhappy together. We're in America and it's almost the 21st century. Divorce is no longer disgraceful as it was in Taiwan in the 60's. Your mom looks good at 66. She gained a bit of weight and her face is fuller. The blemishes from the small pox are almost invisible and she has the well-educated look. If you cannot talk to her, I will talk to her when she comes back. My friend's uncle is a retired professor and a widower. Who knows, they may make a good couple. So, if your father wants to leave, let him go. Your mother deserves to be happy. She won't be alone. We are here for her."

On the airplane

It would not be a long flight. However, Shu-hua 書華 was delighted that the ever thoughtful Jason had gotten an aisle seat for her. It would be easy for her to get in and out of her seat to use the restroom. She put the safety belt on and allowed her mind to wander freely and this alone would be a treat. She was always tense when Ha-en 海安 was near, although he only beat her in the first few months of their marriage. She believed that only his need of a son made him stop hitting her, but he sure had a barbed wire tongue.

He had courted her so ardently that she could not understand how he became her abuser. When he worked on the ocean liner, he spent thirty days on the ship and ten days at home. It was great when they were newlyweds. She became pregnant almost immediately. Then one day he came home drunk and she complained a bit when she had to clean him up and tried to advise him not to drink too much. He got mad and hit her, called her "bossy and nagging". After the third time he beat her, it seemed to get easier. She was still teaching at the time and she had tried very hard to cover the bruises. Her best friend advised her to get a divorce but she was afraid that a divorce will shame her family and her mother would be outraged that she had been abused. She was also afraid that her hard-headed brothers would beat up Ha-en海安. Besides, she just knew that Ha-en wouldn't give her the baby, and her parents were having a hard time financially raising her younger siblings. When she almost lost the baby, the beating mercifully stopped.

The reminiscence made her eyes moisten and she murmured, "*I should not have had an affair with another man when I was married. But it's his fault, he pushed me into it.*' The remembrance of her week-long wild romance made her blush and she smiled, '*I'm glad that I had it. It can only come once in a lifetime. I'm lucky. How many women or men would never know true love?*'

She had secretly relived that week again and again when Ha-en was not around. It always gave her the strength to carry on. Once

64

her son Jason found her in her reverie and told her, "Mom. You are absolutely beautiful." She must have blushed and smiled dreamily just now, because a stewardess came by and asked her whether she was alright. She was embarrassed and said, "I'm fine."

She likes to write. Once she had thought about writing it down, but she dropped the idea. She feels that it's almost sacrilegious to put something so beautiful on paper. Besides, she does not know enough words. "*It's all mine. I have his son and that's enough for me.*" Sometimes she even feels that the accident, which caused his death, was essential to making it whole and special.

John, the second son

John waited for his mother at the airport. He missed her; the last time he went to see his parents was almost a year ago. He was secretly glad that his father had decided not to come with her mother. He has known that his father loves his brother more. It hurt him a lot when his father showered his brother with love and not him. All these years he studied so hard and got all 'A's' on his report cards just to please his father. His father's 'praise' was so superficial that it was almost an insult. It truly hurt and he did not know 'why'; and his mother's suffering was painful to see. He knows that he does not look like his father at all. His mother was too eager to tell everyone that he looks like his maternal grandpa and uncles. His brother Jason loves him and always tries to bring his father and him closer.

For a long time he guessed that he might not be his father's son, but whose son is he then? Once when his father was at sea, he walked in on his mother holding a picture of a tall young man with his arm around her. He asked his mother about the man. His mother told him that the man in the picture was his uncle and she put away the photo very quickly. He knew then that his mother was lying. His mother has three brothers; one is 2 years older than her and the other two are 4 and 6 years younger than her. Her older brother is the shortest man in the family, and the man in the picture is tall and much older than either one of his mother's younger brothers. His uncle would never have put his arm around his mother in that intimate manner. John believes that the man in the picture might

65

be his real father but that's something he could not ask his mother or anyone else. Who is, or was, he? Was he married at that time? Is he still alive? Is he the cause of his parents' unhappiness? He must know. He never told his brother about that picture. '*It's almost the 21ˢᵗ century now and the truth of my parentage would not be an embarrassment anymore. Oh! My poor mother had to put up with Ha-en海安 all these years because she did not want me to be an illegitimate bastard. No wonder I am the needle in my father's eyes. He raised me and I should be grateful.*' He decided that he would confront his mother soon in his father's absence.

Shu-hua and her new friend

Shu-hua 書華 was very grateful to have two nice daughters-in-law. Jason's wife, Anna, is a bit stout and candid. John's wife, Jean, is petite and quiet with warm eyes. Shu-hua wished that she could better communicate with Jean but she knew that her English is limited to just simple words and she was not sure that she could say her name right. The younger Chinese all have American names now. To her surprise, Jean came out of the kitchen and greeted her in Mandarin and hugged her. John said proudly, "Mom, Jean took a course at the university to learn Chinese just for you."

Jean said in Chinese, "I practice now." The order of the sentence was wrong and sounded funny. Everyone laughed. Shu-hua found that she could really laugh now. She was glad that Ha-en did not come and she started to enjoy her 'freedom'. She thought, "*Why should I be afraid that he may leave me. To be alone actually is a treat.*"

Jean's mother, Ceo, drove by in the afternoon. She is a widow and lives close by. Shu-hua met her at the young couple's wedding and found her a very friendly and warm person. She took Shu-hua to the mall to shop and she gave Shu-hua her opinions with easygoing and frank manners. Shu-hua found in her a ready friend. They enjoyed each other's company. Shu-hua thought, '*See, I can be happy without a husband.*' She felt more and more positive that she would actually prefer Ha-en to leave. '*I can divorce him, too.*' She was shocked that she could think about this revolutionary idea and she liked it very much indeed.

The three of them sat in the waiting room of the hospital to wait for the delivery of the precious package. It was a robust boy who came into the world with a loud cry. The Chinese call the paternal grandma '*Naenae*奶奶' and the maternal grandma '*Loulo* 姥姥'. Shu-hua is奶奶, and Ceo is *Loulou* 姥姥. Both *Naenae*奶奶 and *Loulou* 姥姥 fussed over Jean and the baby and made sure that all their needs were met. They talked and laughed while working together. Shu-hua enjoyed every minute of it. Her age and her unhappiness melted away. John suddenly found his mother younger and happier. He decided to hold back his questions about his birth for a little while.

Shu-hua 書華 enjoyed holding the baby and thought the baby's nose and wide forehead resembles Wu-mu's吳莫. The young engineer with whom she had an intense weeklong relationship. Chinese people have a somewhat flat nose with a low bridge. Wu-mu's吳莫 nose was high bridged, longer and narrower. He told her that there had been many Jews in his hometown, Kaifeng, Hanan Province ever since the Jews crucified Jesus. Wu-mu吳莫 might have Jewish blood. He wanted to marry her as soon as she divorce Ha-en, but he died in an accident while building the needed highway through the mountains.

She was more relaxed now and her confused thoughts untangled and became clear. Now she was certain that Ha-en knew that John is not his son all along. That's why he never loves John the way he loves Jason, his own son. She now sees clearly that Ha-en planned to leave her and she will have to live alone from now on. '*Do I really mind being alone? I was afraid of it before, but not anymore. I think I actually will enjoy being alone. I have paid enough to give John a father. I will tell John the truth soon.*'

Shu-hua asked Ceo about being alone. Ceo said, "Not bad at all. Of course I miss Jean's stepfather but I enjoy the freedom and independence more. You know a Chinese man of our generation considers himself the boss. He will do everything to secure his authority. We, the Chinese women, have to literally walk on tiptoes around the man in the house in order to keep peace. What a price a woman has to pay. I'm my own boss now. Some German and

Japanese men are no better than the Chinese men. Of course, not everyman is that way. Jean's stepfather was German, and he was alright. It is important for a woman living alone but not be isolated, to make new friends and enjoy living on our own terms." Shu-hua was ready to take her new friend Ceo into her confidence. But before she could, Jason called and told her that Ha-en went back to China and left her a short letter.

Ha-en海安 wrote a letter

Ha-en海安 arranged the bank book and left the lease agreement of the cottage on the kitchen table. He added up the money stored in the refrigerator and in the shoebox under his bed, then divided the amount and put the money into two envelopes. He put one envelope, after wrapping it with two layers of tinfoil, back into the freezer part of the refrigerator. He put the other envelope and the money he had withdrawn from the bank, into a carefully sewn hidden pocket on the inside of his undershirt. The total amount was $3200. He then put a bit more than $200 and the plane tickets into his wallet. Everything was ready for him to go to the airport. There was plenty of time before his scheduled flight, so he sat down and began to write the farewell letter to his wife.

Ha-en海安 was not an educated man and he hardly ever had the need to write a letter. Shu-hua 書華 wrote all the important correspondence for the family. He always resented that Shu-hua was better educated than him. He felt inferior to her and then felt the need to control and belittle her.

Ha-en was not a good student when he was young. His father hired a scholar to teach him, but he did not want to learn. It was Lijei李姐 who taught him the few words he could write before he left China at age 15. *'Oh. Lijei李姐, are you really alive? Do you still remember me? I'm coming back to you! I choose you over my son's mother.'*

He actually did not know her name. 'Li'李 is her last name and 'Jei'姐 simply means 'elder sister'. Lijei李姐 was an abandoned baby because she had cleft lip and was considered 'bad luck'. The village's old Dr. Li李 found her nearly drowning in a ditch. Dr. Li and his wife had no children and they raised the deformed baby girl as their own. Nobody knew where she came from or her birthday. Dr. Li thought that she was around five months old when he found her and he gave her his last name. Lijei李姐 was taller than the girls and boys of the same age in the villages around and she was big-boned. Dr. Li李 assumed that she was from Northern China. Lijei was smart and a quick learner. Dr. Li taught her vocabulary, herbal medicine and medical skills. The man who Ha-en met a year ago in the restaurant told him that Lijei李姐was not molested and killed by the Communists because she was deformed and she has medical skills. Ha-en prayed that it was true, so he could go back to find Lijei or learn what happened to her. Ha-en loved her. It was that kind of innocent, pure love one could only have as a young child.

Ha-en's mother died when he was 14 years old. His father's concubine abused Ha-en and ordered a servant to beat him behind his father's back. One day the beaten and starving Ha-en hid at a foothill and cried. Lijei李姐 found him and brought him to Dr. Li's home, dressed his wounds and fed him. She was at least half a year older than Ha-en海安 and he called her 'jei'姐, elder sister. Ha-en hanged around Dr. Li's home whenever he could. The kind doctor taught them both every day. Lijei taught him the basics and also coaxed him to learn more.

One day, Ha-en's stepmother kept him home to do some chore. He went out later and saw that four village boys were attacking Lijei李姐, tearing at her clothes. Ha-en helped her fight them off. It was a hard fight. Ha-en was a fierce fighter and Lijei was a strong girl. They repelled the attackers and Lijei collapsed and cried in his arms. He was her protector. From then on, they were inseparable in their innocent love. He could never forget the way Lijei looked at him with her crystal clear eyes, so full of encouragement, affection and admiration. Her image was deeply etched into his mind. All these years later, she still appears in his dreams. He was attracted to Shu-hua 書華 because she also has those beautiful clear eyes. But Shu-hua could never replace Lijei, Ha-en's first love. Ha-en felt sorry for Shu-hua and he also felt guilty that he had abused her in the beginning.

When Jason, his first son, was six months old, Ha-en was working in the boiler room on a big ocean liner. There was an explosion. He almost died and the ship doctor nursed him back to life and told him that his injury was internal. He could have a normal life, but he could not father a child any more. He was too proud to tell Shu-hua the truth the first time he came home. She was pregnant when he was home the next month. So he knew John was not his son. He wanted to have a divorce, but then he heard about the accidental death of a young engineer and his crew. Then he knew he could not divorce her. In the 60's, adultery was a serious social taboo and she would not have any chance of finding a job or another husband if the truth be known. She was the mother of his only child. He also felt deep down that it's his fault and she was not the only one to blame. So, he never told her that he knew all along and that it's hard to love John, who was the living proof of his wife's infidelity and for more than 30 years he's worn a 'green hat'[1]. He murmured, '*No more*'. Ha-en looked at the clock, quickly wrote a short note and left.

The note read, "I knew John is not my son but I'm the guilty one, too. I left you half of the money we had, the cottage to live in, and two sons who will take care of you. I'm going back home to find the girl I loved almost 60 years ago. If I cannot find her, I will come back to you if you still want me. Ha-en. I am so sorry."

-End-

Afterwards

They never heard from Ha-en again and no one knows exactly where his home village is. John arranged for a lawyer to help him change his last name to "Wu" 吳. He found that he may have an aunt in Texas and an uncle in Taiwan. Shu-hua and Ceo became close friends and they planned to help each other to write their memoirs.

---

1   Wear a green hat: A Chinese slang term for a husband whose wife has an extramarital affair.

Jeopardy

Historical background

"Chinese" (中國人) is a collective term for many ethnic groups. The five largest groups are: Han漢, Manchu滿Mongolian蒙Muslims 回and Tibetans藏. Han (漢) is the original and majority group of the Chinese people. They occupied the middle section of modern China, which is comprised of the vast area along two long rivers - the Yellow River黃河 to the north, and the Yangtze River揚子 江 to the south. They built the Great Wall in 202 B.C. to prevent invasions from the nomadic Manchu and Mongolian tribes from the north. At the end of the 10ᵗʰ century, the Han's Tang Dynasty (唐朝) weakened. None of the warlords were strong enough to unite the whole country. The Mongols breached the Great Wall and seized upon sixteen counties; including Yenjing (present day Beijing 北 京). In 937 A.D., Yenjing became the capital of the Mongolian Dynasty, the Liao (遼) Dynasty. At the same period, a succession of Han states occupied the area south of the Yangtze River, until the Song Dynasty (宋朝) united the South. The Emperor of the Song Dynasty strived to defeat the Liao, to regain the historically significant capital city of Yenjing, and the Great Wall. Recurrent battles occurred along the borders.

****

Jeopardy

Empress Dowager of the Liao States (遼) paced along the veranda encircling the administration hall in the sprawling palaces of Yenjing.

She often came here in the afternoon to relax, but today, she came over right after the morning administration meeting. Two pieces of ominous news troubled her greatly. The first was that the Emperor of the Song Dynasty (宋朝) wanted to wage war on Liao (遼) to recover the sixteen counties that the Liao seized upon years ago. The second was that another group of Mongols to the west showed definite ambition of conquering all of China. The Empress Dowager must find a way to protect her country.

Her grandmother was a Han漢woman, so she was shorter, fairer skinned and more fragile-looking than the average Mongolian women. Under her deceivingly delicate demeanor, she was shrewd and strong. Her quick-wittedness and cheerful manners won her the Emperor's affection and she became one of his favorites. She gave birth to Princess Pearl, and she raised a boy from another minor concubine who died soon after giving birth. Her husband, the Emperor, had three sons and one of them was the Queen's. Usually, the Queen's son should succeed the throne. Somehow she charmed and coaxed the Emperor to choose her adopted son as the crown prince and the heir apparent.

Eight years ago, her adopted son, the young Emperor, died in a hunting accident. The only heir, her grandson, was only four years old at that time. At fifty, she had to ruthlessly put down another royal prince's coup d'état, and then she ruled the State of Liao as the Regent of the child Emperor. It was a challenge to rule a politically unsteady, economically weak country when the newly founded Han's Song Dynasty to the south and the Manchu to the northeast attacked them often. Six years ago, she bribed a corrupt Song general to set up a trap to isolate and annihilate the Song's elite General Yang's 楊 force. The defeated Song was forced to agree to a peace treaty with her. She also kept the Manchu滿of the northeast out of the Great Wall.

She ruled wisely with the help of her trusted vassals, and she treated the captured Han and Manchu people with fairness. The State of Liao became prosperous during the period of peace with the Song Dynasty. Her people, the Mongols, admired, absorbed, and emulated the Han culture. In Yenjing, the Han, the Mongols and the Manchu lived in harmony, and the city was flourishing.

The new threats made her edgy. She walked faster and her steps became heavier. Her countenance was drawn and pinched. She ordered, "Summon the Prime Minister and the Generalissimo."

The Generalissimo was her brother; the Prime Minister was her brother-in-law. The three of them conferred for a long time.

"I agree this may not be the best course we can take. I wish we could find another way. But time is crucial. We must stop them. Let's hope it will work. We just cannot defend two, or possibly three, fronts at the same time," Empress Dowager concluded.

The Prime Minister said, "Even a truce will definitely buy us some time to prepare our military force. Meanwhile, we'll find a way to stop, or at least to slow down, the unification of the new Mongolian uprising to the west. If all of the Mongolian tribes there unify, they will be undefeatable. Of course, we have the Great Wall to keep them out, but defending the long Wall will surely drain our military forces. It has only been three generations since our people lived together with the Han, and we have gone soft from too much of the Han's influence. We're more sophisticated and civilized now, but we have lost some of our bravery. We need time to reshape our forces."

The Dowager nodded in agreement.

Her brother, the Generalissimo, said, "Lately, more Mongolian women have been walking a half step behind their husbands in the Han people's style. I bet that many Mongolian women cannot ride a horse or shoot a straight arrow now." He then continued, "But, if we have to do it this way, what about Princess Pearl…"

The Dowager snapped, "Be quiet! I know what I'm doing; I'm her mother." Somehow, her tone changed from adamant at first, to something between sad and remorseful.

A eunuch reported, "Your Majesty, important military dispatch came. General Xiu requests an immediate audience."

She replied, "We'll hear him, and that's settled. Call Captain Situ."

Situ only had a left arm. His aunt was Princess Pearl's wet nurse and she, not the Empress Dowager, took care of Princess Pearl like a true mother. The Dowager assigned Situ as the head of the Princess's personal guards. One of his duties was to periodically inform the Dowager of the daily affairs of the Princess Pearl's household, especially the coming and going of the Princess's husband, Mu-nee 木易, a captured Han漢officer. Situ knew Mu-nee's true identity; he did not relish his duty of spying on him. He disliked the new order the Dowager put him up to even more, but an order from the Dowager could not be ignored. ' *Ahe! That short old lady sure is shrewd. She bought a Song traitor to eliminate the famous General Yang楊 and forced the humiliated late Emperor of Song into a peace treaty. When she noticed that all of us are sorry at Yang's honorable suicide, she then deliberately leaked the information of the treachery to the Emperor of Song and got the traitor killed. To win goodwill on both sides, She also ordered a great memorial built to honor the famous General Yang楊. She definitely knew Mu-nee's true identity and still allowed him to marry Princess Pearl. I always wondered why she did that. I wonder what trick she is up to now.*'

Unlike her mother, Princess Pearl was tall and homely. Also, unlike her calculating mother, she was friendly and kind. Everyone liked Princess Pearl. Her father died when she was seventeen years old. Two of her brothers were fighting for the throne and the royal families were split. No one was safe. Then, her mother arranged for her to marry one of the able captains of the opposite force. It was her husband and her loyal supporters that helped her mother to gain the final victory. A year later, her husband died on the battlefield when the Manchu from the northeast tried to breach the Great Wall.

She did not stay a widow for long. Six years ago, Situ saved and his nursed the dying Mu-nee back to life. Princess Pearl married him. They now have a three years old girl and an infant son. They were a loving couple. Mu-nee was cultured and soft spoken. Unlike the other rowdy Mongolian officers, he never brawled at the wine shop or kept other women on the side. Princess Pearl was truly happy and the walls of her court could not contain the laughter and joyful sounds within.

74

Although there were maids and wet nurses, Princess Pearl liked to care for her children herself. She was holding her crying infant son and cooing him, when the very distressed Mu-nee walked in.

Princess Pearl inquired, "What's the matter? You look worried."

Mu-nee answered, "Nothing... but... I heard...." He hesitated at first, and then told his wife the truth and asked for her help. "Mu-nee木易 is not my real name. I'm Yang Sye-lang楊四郎, the fourth son of the late General Yang. My brother Yang Leo-lang楊六郎 (the sixth son) is a Song General. I heard that he is leading a military campaign against the Liao state. Their force has already advanced to only 100 *li* (里miles) south of the border. My whole family is at the camp. I want to go down there to see my mother.... and..." He hesitated again, "...and my first wife. She was pregnant six years ago. I may have a child. I want to go down there to see them. I promise I'll be back. It's only for one night. I'll be back by dawn. Please help me! Will you steal a military pass for me to go? You can put it back and no one would know. Oh! I really have no right to ask you to do this. I better not go. It's just that my mother might think that I'm dead. You know two of my older brothers and my father all died six years ago. My half brother might be dead, too. I want my mother to know that I'm alive and well. I want her to know that I have a loving wife and kids."

Princess Pearl stared at him open-mouthed. She protested at first and then gave in. She said, "What if you don't want to come back?" Mu-nee swore, "Lighting and thunder will strike me down if I don't come back to you." It was a dangerous and treasonous endeavor and Empress Dowager might kill all of them. They embraced and their mingling tears dripped on the head of their crying infant son.

The autumn wind blew the fine yellow sand from the northwest and whistled softly at dusk. Just a short distance outside the South Gate of Yenjing (Beijing), Yang Sye-lang楊四郎 paced back and forth. He wondered if he had jeopardized the lives that were dear to him. Princess Pearl, his children and many others who had helped him were all in danger. He almost wished that he had never thought about it. At this moment, he would rather have Princess Pearl failed at the attempt. But, what if she got caught in the act? The Dowager will not show mercy, not even to spare her own daughter's life. It's true that Princess Pearl was Empress Dowager's only child, and the old woman doted upon her grandchildren. But, she just could not pardon her daughter's treasonous act of stealing a top military security pass. Without the pass, he could not cross the border to visit his mother at the Song camp.

The knee-high leather boots he wore were too big and he nearly tripped over a fallen branch. The nomadic Mongolian was huskier and taller than the domestic Han people. Every piece of battle attire that Situ had provided him was slightly big and loose on him, even though he was considered a tall man among the Han people. The long bow and the leather bag full of arrows, capped with sharp metal, felt heavy on his shoulder, but the sheathed double-edged long and curved saber with thin blades felt light. He knew that the bow and arrow were the primary weapons of the Manchu and Mongolian people. They only used the saber for hand-to-hand combat. He missed his own three-pronged long spear and wished he had on a metal breastplate and helmet, instead of the silk headgear and padded vest he had on. '*Oh, well,*' he thought, '*they designed their battle gear for swiftness.' And the mirror-like texture of the raw silk could definitely make the enemy's arrows slip. Situ was a Liao officer before he lost his arm. He knew what I would need for this trip. I think he may have been wounded fighting my late father's company,*" Yang Sye-lang楊四郎 frowned. '*Situ must know my true identity now. Princess Pearl must have told him. But Situ sometimes looks at me in an odd way and I wonder whether we had previously met on the battlefield.*'

Situ and a guard arrived with four saddled horses and handed him a half-piece of dazzling, arrow-shaped gold plate with some Mongol words etched on it. It was a military security pass and its jagged edges had to be a perfect match with its other half. It also had a piece of bright scarlet silk cord.

Situ saluted, "Your Highness, Princess Pearl got the highest priority night pass for you, and I also brought you the spare horses. I pray that all the gods of heaven and earth grant you a swift return by dawn, and then the Princess can return the pass before its absence is noticed. Our lives depend on the pass's timely return. Remember this: tonight's password is 'cold desert wind', and tomorrow's password is "purple cloud'." Following Situ's instruction, Yang Sye-lang楊四郎 tied the pass securely as a Mongolian officer would do. He replied, "Thank you. I'm grateful for all the help. Trust me, I'll be back by dawn, and I know the risk and thus the consequences very well."

"Come with me. I have something else for you." Situ walked to a spare horse and took out a long spear from under a length of leather tied along the horse's flank. "Where did you get this? It's mine!" Yang Sye-lang楊四郎 shouted. It was his long spear. Six years ago, he had thrown his spear away with all his remaining strength. He did not want the enemy to identify him. He, his father, and his brothers were surrounded and outnumbered by the Liao's main force when the Song traitor, General Pan, deliberately held back reinforcements. Two of his brothers died and his father were captured. When the Liao's generalissimo, the Empress Dowager's brother, offered his father a high standing position and rewards if his father surrendered. His father refused and committed suicide. The Mongols respected his bravery and an honorable memorial was built for father and sons following a grand funeral.

Situ chuckled, "Surprise! I have always known who you really were. I kept quiet until you told Princess Pearl the truth. Captain Yang 楊. I knew it years ago when my men found you unconscious. You only had your underwear on. I ordered my men to keep their mouths shut when they found your abandoned battle gown and spear in the cornfield. My aunt nursed you back to life and then, lucky you, the Princess married you."

"But, I…" Yang Sye-lang楊四郎 wondered, '*in my underwear. Who undressed me? And why?*' he stuttered, "Why? Why did you save me? I'm your enemy."

"Your late father, the most revered General Yang楊, spared my life nine years ago somewhere south of here. The Liao General who led us at that time was a coward. He ordered a hasty withdrawal without a fight as soon as he saw your father's banner. A small company of us was cut down, but your father forbade his men to kill us. He even let his doctor attend to our wounds before he released us. I lost an arm but I owe him my life. A lot of us were genuinely sorry that your father and your two brothers were dead. I want, at least, to save one of his sons." Situ lied, "Your secret is safe with me. I did not report it back then. But I think Her Majesty had guessed it. She won't let her daughter marry a nobody." Yang Sye-lang 楊四郎 said, "My father would never kill the defenseless and wounded. I'm very grateful that you've saved me and now you're helping me."

Situ sighed and then continued, "You got to show your own spear with the banner on it when you are close to the Song宋 camp, lest the Song宋 soldiers kill you. You better hurry. The first night bell will sound soon and we must get back before the city gate closes. At dawn, I'll wait for you here. Good luck and BE BACK BY DAWN." Situ then reassured Yang Sye- Lang, "No need to worry, just flash your pass and firmly order the soldiers at the check point, and you'll be fine. We have quite a few high-ranking Han 漢 officers now. Our kind Empress Dowager rescinded the law of killing captured Han officers; instead, she has offered them good positions and rewards."

Situ reentered the city gate just before it was closed and met his awaiting aunt. He whispered, "Is Princess Pearl all right?" The old woman answered, "She cried herself to sleep. Ahe! How could a mother do something like that?" Situ said, "We all are pawns, aren't we? She will do anything to keep our country safe."

Riding hard, Yang Sye-Lang楊四郎 heard the first night bell and the warning "Beware of fire! Beware of theft" as he was crossing the long, low bridge. He thought, '*Ahe! The city gate is closed. The Mongols really admire the Han culture. They have adopted the system of sounding five night bells from dusk to the first rooster's crow. The city gate will open again tomorrow at dawn. I must hurry'*

The road was blocked at the end of the bridge. It was a Liao (遼) checkpoint. Yang flashed the pass, ordered the barricades to be removed, changed to a fresh horse and dashed southward. The officers in charge acknowledged the priority pass readily; they did not even ask him the passwords.

Yang Sye-lang 楊四郎 changing to a fresh horse at two other checkpoints and pushing hard. He contemplated peace. He thought, 'I hope that the new Song宋 Emperor does not really intend to go to war with the Liao (遼). *Maybe it's just his way of showing off his power and military strength. There are rumors that he might be responsible for his brother's death. There is no proof. I hope that he wants peace. Everyone benefits in peace, but suffers in war. I beg all the gods to grant us peace and let our children have a chance to grow up.'*

Six years ago, he had seen his 2nd and 3rd brother being killed. Now he wondered whether his 5th brother, separated from him during the battle, had escaped or died. His youngest brother, Yang Leo-lang楊六郎married the present Song Emperor's half-sister, a Song 宋 Princess, and thus had not fought in that disastrous campaign. Now, Yang Leo-lang楊六郎 led the Song army, so the whole family would be at the camp. All the women in his family, except the Song Princess, came from military families. They had followed the legendary female general Hua Mu-lan's花木蘭 example and could fight as fiercely as men. But the frequent campaigns took a heavy toll on the women and many children died young.

It got colder and the fine, windblown sand pierced his face. Yang Sye-lang Sye-lang楊四郎 started to appreciate that the long flap of his headgear draped over his shoulders to protect his neck. The whining of the wind sounded like some wounded soldiers' yells of pain before death. The trees and houses he galloped by stood like the soldiers' spears and over-thrown chariots.

'Aye! So much death! My only nephew, sixth brother's son, should be about fourteen years old now. I wish I could bring my first wife back to the north with me. Will my mother forgive me for not fighting for the Song? Will she understand that I have to go back to Liao? His thoughts darted here and there when he heard the second night bell and saw the Song宋outpost and banners ahead.

Sensing an attack, Yang Sye-lang blocked the blow with the Mongol saber and its thin blades snapped. Someone had attacked him with a heavy steel staff and he knew only one man who was powerful enough to brandish such a heavy weapon. He readily recognized his half-brother Yang Wu-lang (5th Son) 楊五郎 and who must have been the one who removed his Song uniform at the terrible battlefield six years ago.

"Brother." They both called simultaneously. They stared at each other speechlessly and their eyes swam with tears. They were tears of sorrow for their deceased family, but also tears of joy that they both were alive.

"Ahe! You escaped. But, why are you wearing a monk's habit?" Yang Sye-lang 楊四郎 asked.

"Brother, I felt completely empty when my mother and wife died of that terrible plague; our father and brothers' death was the last straw. I'm tired of the pointless fighting. A monk saved me six years ago, so I am a monk now. You have the Liao uniform on. Did you surrender to them?"

"Of course not. It's a long story and I don't have time to go into the details. Let's hurry to our sixth brother's camp. A lot of lives depend on it and I must make haste."

"Who goes there?" A slender, young Han漢 officer outfitted in full battle gear ordered his battalion of soldiers to surround them. The officer sounded young and Yang Sye-lang 楊四郎 assumed that they had met their nephew.

"Tz Bo, call your men off. We are your uncles. Take us to your father immediately," ed.

"But, my uncles are all dead. How do you now my first name!"

A soldier said, "Captain, don't trust them. They might be your uncles, but now they are Liao's (遼) spies for sure."

Yang Sye-lang said, "We would never fight or spy for the Liao. I must see your father at once. Your grandma *Shia* would be thrilled to know that both of us are alive." To further convince his nephew, he mentioned his mother's maiden name, which only the immediate family would know.

On their way to headquarter, Yang Sye-lang楊四郎 noticed that most of the Song宋soldiers were young boys. He recalled that the Liao (遼) army was full of young recruits too. The battle of seizing Yenjing (Beijing) six years ago caused heavy casualties on both sides. If another war occurred soon, most of the young ones would probably not reach twenty. He hoped that he could convince his sixth brother into agreeing to a peace treaty. The Liao (遼) wanted peace and abhorred war.

It was a tearful reunion. Yang Sye-lang was glad to see that his sixty-five years old mother walked with a straight back and a warrior's gait. His first wife looked tired and both of his younger sisters were married now.

His sixth brother楊六郎 seemed extremely interested in how and why Situ had helped his brother's visit. Yang Sye-lang told his family that their late father saved Situ nine years ago.

His mother said, "Never mind that Situ now. I'm glad that the Empress Dowager treats you well and the Liao Princess sounds like a very good wife to you too. But, I don't want you to go back to them. Your primary loyalty should be to your own country and your family as Confucius had taught us. Besides, your wife misses you terribly. Your son was a stillborn. You cannot ignore your duty to be a good husband to her."

"But, Neon (mother), I have to go back before dawn lest they kill the Princess, your grandchildren and many others who helped me to come here to see you. If there is peace, I might be able to visit you again. Princess Pearl agreed that I could bring my first wife up north. Don't you think I'm not agonized over where my loyalty should be! I beg you to let me go and I must make haste," Yang Sye-lang pleaded.

"Neon (mother,) I beg you to let him go. We must save your grandchildren. They may kill the Liao Princess. If not, I cannot bear to think what a miserable life the Liao Princess would have. Please let him go. I just wish that he could come back to see us again," Yang Sye-lang's楊四郎 first wife said.

"Thank you, my dear wife. I won't ever forget you and I'll try to get you up north." Yang Sye-lang bowed to her.

The third bell sounded. One of his younger sisters begged him to stay. She said, "My 5th 五 Brother will stay. How can't you? The Liao will kill you."

Yang Leo-lang楊六郎 said, "No need to worry. 4ᵗʰ四Brother won't be killed if we don't attack first. He is a….. I will order free spare horses."

Yang Sye-lang 楊四郎 kowtowed to his mother one more time and then dashed out.

A while later, Yang Leo-lang (6ᵗʰ son) told his mother, "I double-checked the war record just now. Nine years ago, Dye (father) was stationed on the west front, which is far away from the vicinities of Yenjing (Beijing)."

The old woman sighed, "I know. So, he is a pawn all right. His wife and my grand children are hostages. How can the shrewd Empress Dowager of the Liao (遼) let anyone steal a top security pass? Now we know for sure that Liao wants peace."

"Yes, my intelligence informed me that another Mongolian tribe from the west would be ready to attack the Liao (遼) soon."

Yang Sye-lang楊四郎 dashed north with an uneasy mind. He was afraid that he would not be back in Yenjing before dawn. Also, the way his sixth brother said that the Dowager would not kill him kept on nagging him.

The first rooster crowed and the night bell sounded five times.

When Yang Sye-lang reached the Liao checkpoint, the waiting Liao (遼) soldiers arrested him. In a flash, he came to a full understanding.

He was immediately tied to a post. His crying daughter, Situ and his men, and the Princess's nanny were all tied to posts to be executed outside the South Gate of Yenjing. With the crying boy in her arm, Princess Pearl kneeled in the dirt in front of the enraged Empress Dowager.

"Archers! Ready!" Her Majesty's voice was loud and clear. The silent crowd watched.

"Hold! Wait…." The Prime Minister called and approached the Dowager. They talked quietly for a while and Her Majesty, seemingly reluctant, called, "Let them go. Double the surveillance on the traitor Yang Sye-lang 楊四.郎Shoot him at once if he dares to escape. Put them under house arrest for three months. Dismissed."

Yang Sye-lang楊四郎 sighed, "Princess, the play is over and the curtain has fallen. I'm going to take off my costume. Let's go home." He picked up his daughter.

"Yes, my husband," Princess walked a couple of steps behind and a wet nurse carried the boy in tow. She murmured, *"Why did he say that for? I wonder…"*

Two months later, Song宋 and Liao (遼signed a peace treaty.

In her secret chamber, the Dowager smiled to her brother and the Prime Minister, "It worked perfectly. Now we can concentrate on preparing our defense against the eastbound Genghis Khan and his formidable horde of savages."

"Congratulation, Your Majesty. Having Situ planted in the Princess's palace was the winning touch. Although, I am weary of that cunning Situ. He could be a formidable adversary someday."

She sighed, "I bet by now Yang Sye-lang楊四郎 has seen through the ploy, and he would never believe that Princess Pearl is truly innocent."

"We could get his first wife here to make sure he stays."

"Let's make it look like my daughter's idea. He will be in her debt."

-End-

Afterward: Years later, Genghis Khan's grandson, Kublai Khan, ruled China as the first Emperor of the Yuan (Mongol) Dynasty (元朝), while his cousins ruled Moscow, India and the present-day Middle East.

Wu Zixu's 伍子胥 escape. – His hair turned white overnight.

Historical background--The Spring and Autumn Period (春秋時期 770 BC to 476 BC) of Chinese history refers to the first half of the East Chou Dynasty (东周). Thirty-some vassal states warred on each other often. The Emperor or a king himself alone held the supreme power to promote or kill at will a general, a minister, or even his sons. In this story, Wu Zixu. 伍子胥 escaped from the persecution of King Ping楚平王.

Wu Zixu's 伍子胥 escape. – His hair turned white overnight.

King Ping楚平王 was a wicked and pleasure-seeking king of the state of Chu楚 in 528 B.C. He trusted his equally villainous and greedy minister Fei Wou-Ki费无极 who would please the King unscrupulously without any regard for morality. When Fei 费went to The State Of Qing to pick up Prince Zijian's建 promised bride, he saw that the bride was rare. Fei费 plot to please the lustful King Ping平王, and manipulated to have the bride entered the King's palace, not Prince Zijian's.建. The immoral and *lascivious* King Ping 平王took his future daughter-in-law as a new wife himself. A maid married Prince Zijian建 instead. The broom and the bride would not meet before the marriage in a traditional arranged marriage. Prince Zijian建 and no one else knew the substitution.

On Fei's费suggestion, King Ping sent Prince Zijian建 to a city far away from his capital with the sole purpose of covering up his immoral deed. Each of the new wives had a son. However, the revolting secret leaked gradually. The young queen, who should

84

be a daughter-in-law, now knew the defile act. She often lamented that she had married an old king instead of a young prince. The indigent Prince Zijian 建 thought, "That evil Fei费 bewitched my father, the King, into this incestuous act. I will kill him." At the same time, King Ping 平王wanted to placate his unhappy young queen and promised her that her son would be the hire apparent, not Prince Zijian建. King Ping coerced Professor Wu, Prince Zijian's建 tutor, to kill the Prince discreetly. Professor Wu criticized the King's immoral act and helped Prince Zijian建 to escape. King Ping wanted to kill Professor Wu. Fei费 advised, "Both of Professor Wu's sons are capable of revenge; we must lull them here and kill them all."

Professor Wu had two sons. Wu Zixu 伍子胥 was the younger one. They were at their hometown, and they knew neither their father's arrest nor Prince Zijian's 建 escape. A letter from their father said, "I am in jail for disobeying the will of King Ping. King Ping wants to have you two here to help me to complete his order. Then we, all three of us, will be pardoned and rewarded. Come at once."

Wu Zixu's 伍子胥brother said, "We should go right away."

Wu Zixu 伍子胥replied, "No, We must not go. Father must have criticized *King Ping's horrible act, and that evil* Fei费 must have forced our father to write this letter to get us both there. If we do go, King Ping will kill the three of us. If we do not go, they might be afraid that we will avenge our father and dare not act rashly to kill our father."

His brother said, "I will go like a son should obey his father. King Ping平王 *might be regretful and remorseful for his wrong and pardon us. Besides, my going will give you, more capable than I, more time to escape. Don't tell me where you are going, so no torture could make me tell.*"

Fei Wou-Ki费无极 coerced and threatened the jailed father and son, "Tell us where Wu zixu伍子胥 is! *We need his bravery and superior military skill to complete an order. I will be direct. Pardon or torture?* "

Professor Wu replied, "*No more lies. You already determined to kill us anyway, so severe torture before death means little to us. Father knows sons, and I know my sons well: My elder son would not* ask, and *Wu zixu would not tell. You are right to be afraid of his revenge.*

Kill us quickly! Why wait?" Fei Wou-ki费无极 ordered an all-out pursuit of Wu Zizhen伍子胥. He ordered posters of *'immediately arrest of Wu Zixu 伍子胥"* with portraits and rewards, and also posters were stating *'death penalty for helping the criminal.'*

Wu Zixu 伍子胥escaped. He could not cross a wide rushing river, and his pursuers were approaching fast.

He took off his robe and shoes and wrote on the sandy beach, "Father, Brother, we will soon meet in the underworld黄泉" and then hid behind a rock. The soldiers saw them and the written words; they presumed that Wu Zixu 伍子胥had jumped into the river to committed suicide. They collected the clothes and reported to Fei 费to claim the rewards, but they received a beating instead. Fei费knew that it was a ruse. He sent more soldiers to go after Wu Zixu 伍子胥 and ordered, "Wu Zixu's 伍子胥must not allowed escaping from Chu State 楚国."

More soldiers at the border searched for anyone who wanted to leave Chu State 楚国. There were posters of arrest Wu Zixu伍子胥 everywhere. Wu Zixu's 伍子胥dared not go near the gate. A man came to him and whispered, *"Master Wu, I will help you. Come with me."* The man was Wu's housekeeper. He said, *"I am selling water now,"* he continued, *"There are two levels on my water cart, You could hide in the lower layer, and I will fill the upper layer with water. I could remove a board from the bottom of the lower level for you to breathe."*

The soldiers at the gate searched the water cart, *"open it up. Let us take a look."* They saw the water and said, *"two containers of water, pay two cash, and you can go, come back soon. We'll close the gate early.*

Wu Zixu joined the exiled Prince Zijian and his young son in Song State宋国. Prince Zijian swore he would kill Fei Wou-Ki 费无极, oust his father the corrupt King Ping楚平王and reclaim the throne that was rightfully his. Fei's费 secret assassins tried to kill them. The two of them and the young boy fled overnight to a small country Zheng郑国 where Prince Zijian was murdered soon afterward. Wu Zixu 伍子胥 and the young boy flee to the Wu 吴国to the northeast. They must pass through the Gate Zha昭关, an immigration checkpoint to leave Chu state 楚国. The checkpoint 昭 关 was a tall and narrow gate with high walls on both sides wedged through high mountains. A general and his soldiers guarded it. There were posters of "arrest Wu Zixu 伍子胥" on the walls. The soldiers checked out everyone who wanted to leave the State of Chu楚国 against the portrait of Wu Zixu's 伍子胥. Wu 伍could not think of a way to get out of the gate without being caught. An old man whispered to him, "*Master Wu, do you want to get out of the country?*" Wu Zixu 伍子胥denied, "*My name is not Wu伍, You've got the wrong person.*" The old man said, "I am Dong 东皋公, a doctor. I saw your portrait, and I'm waiting here to help you. Don't be afraid. Your father had saved my life once. I will help you."

Dr. Dong 东皋公 took Wu Zixu 伍子胥, and the boy to a tool shed in his backyard and said, "*Master Wu, I am sorry that I have to hide you here. The walls have ears, and the servants might talk in the house. Here you will be out of sight. I will have my most trusted servants to bring you meals. I will fetch a good friend here to help you to escape.*"

Wu Zixu 伍子胥 paced all night long and thought, "*Can I trust him, a stranger whom I've just met? Will his friend be trustful? Why does he need to fetch a friend here to help me?*"

When Dr. Dong东皋公 brought them their breakfast and tea the next morning, he said, "*Ah! Your hair! Your hair had turned white overnight! Master Wu, you must have worried. It's my fault that I did not tell you my friend's name, and why do we need him here to help you? My friend Master Huang looks like your double with the same height, same built. The soldiers will think he was you and arrest him. You will have an opportunity to get out of the gate.* Good Good! *Your white hair makes you look like an old man, and it sure makes it easy for you to escape,*" he continued, "*I will make your face looks older. You have to bend and stoop and walk slower.*"

Master Huang arrived, and he indeed resembled Wu Zixu伍子 胥. Three of them perfected the plan for Wu Zixu's伍子胥escape. Dr. Dong东皋公suggested, "Master Wu, You and the young boy were on the run for a while. Fei's men might have noticed it. I will keep the young Prince here and raise him. I want to keep Prince Zijian's 建 bloodline and a future king."

The next morning, the soldiers arrested Master Huang. They shouted excitedly, "We'd *captured Wu Zixu* 伍子胥*. ", and "We will get a big reward!"* Master Huang shouted and denied, "You've *got the wrong person. I am Dr. Dong'* 东皋公 *friend."* The general said, *"I know Dr. Dong, and I will contact him,* "to his soldiers, "Keep on checking! Don't let the real Wu Zixu 伍子胥" getting away."

Wu Zixu 伍子胥 walked out of the gate with an older man's slow gait.

-End-

A stealthy dog, a crowing rooster.

Historical background

The Warring States Period战国 (475 BC-221 BC) was a period of significant change in Chinese history. The Emperors of the Chou Dynasty ruled China in names only. Each of the seven warring vassal states warred on each other until the First Emperor 秦始皇 of the Qing 秦 State unified China in 221 BC. Each vassal state recruited the most capable genius.

A stealthy dog, a crowing rooster

In the turbulent era of the Chinese Warring States Period战国 (475 BC-221 BC), the kings and their advisors of each seven vassal states strived to assemble brilliant and knowledgeable persons in all fields. Tian Wen田文 was the chief adviser of the Chi齐State. He showered the same hospitality and shared the same dishes with his three thousand talented recruits, regardless of whether they were high-born or poor and uneducated. He understood and sympathized with the underprivileged and unwanted people since he was a child.

Tian Wen田文 was born on a legendary unfortunate day, the fifth day of the fifth month of the lunar calendar. Incidentally, the great poet Qu Yum 屈原drowned himself on that particular day in 299 BC. Has been established the Dragon Boats Festival ever since in the great poet's memory. The tourists visiting China can see a magnificent statue of the great poet 屈原 erected in the middle of the mighty Yangtze River. Is it coincident? Anyway, As the story goes, Tian Wen's 田文 father told his mother, "This child will bring us nothing but ruin. Don't feed him." But Tian Wen's mother secretly raised him, and an old scholar taught him. He grew up an accomplished youth. His father changed, recanted his previous superstitions bias, and took Tien Wen back as his heir apparent. The King of Qing秦 State, the great-grandfather of the First Emperor 秦始皇, heard of Tian Wen's reputation and offered Tian Wen's the position of the prime minister. The patriotic Tien Wen田文 declined. He became the top adviser of his home State, Chi齐. Tien Wen 田文 and his militant recruits won battles and expanded the Chi齐 state's territory. His other talented guests also reformed the technology that increased the Chi齐State's salt production. The Chi State齐 grew strong and prosperous. Other ministers were jealous of Tien Wen's田文 success. They advised the King of Chi 齐 either killed or demoted Tien Wen田文lest his powerful group would overthrow the King and sized the Chi齐 State. The King demoted Tien Wen田文.

The Qing 秦 State to the west had to war frequently on the nomad and militant Mongolians. It became the strongest among the seven warring states. The capital, the present-day Xi'an 西安, where the Terracotta Warriors were. Their army conquered and occupied the land of the weak neighboring states. They kidnapped the King of Chu 楚王, and the random consisted of a significant area of land. In 299 BC, King of the Chi 齐 ordered Tien Wen田 文 to go to Xi'an 西安 to negotiate a peace treaty with the Qing 秦 State. Some historians indicated that Tien Wen's 田文 adversaries wanted to have the King of Qing killed him because Tien Wen 田 文 had refused King of Qing's秦王offer before.

Once again, King of Qing秦王asked Tie Wen 田文 to be the prime minister of the Qin State. King Qing 秦王 wanted to have Tien Wen's capable followers to help him to conquer the whole of China sooner His other advisors opposed. They said, "Tian Wen and his followers are indeed very capable, but his loyalty is to his home state, the Chi State 齐. How could we know that he won't sabotage us?" Another said, "We cannot trust him. We better kill him before he and his gang could do us harm." King of Qing 秦王 house arrested Tian Wen and wanted to kill him.

The situation was critical. King of Qing had a favorable courtesan Yan Jade who could plead with the King of Qing for Tian Wen's release. Tian Wen presented her valuables and required her assistance. Lady Yan Jade wanted another white fox's fur robe, which Tien Wen had given to King Qing when he first arrived. It was a rare and a one-of-a-kind precious robe, and King of Quig kept it in a guarded storage room. Tian Wen could not find another one. One of Tian Wen's associate said he could bark like a dog, dig a hole and steal like a dog. He then risked his life and stole the robe late at night. Lady Jade had the robe and pleaded with King Qing to release Tian Wen.

Tian Wen's group fled out of Xi'an just before the city gate was closed for the night. King of Qing regretted soon and immediately sent soldiers to chase after Tian Wen. Their party arrived at Hangu Pass 函谷关 at the border in the middle of the night. By law, the Hangu Pass gate, any city gate, and pass would open when the roosters sounded the first-morning call. Fortunately, one of the associates could imitate the roaster's call well. So, a rooster call came out, and all the roosters around the gate started to crow together. The soldiers at the gate thought that it was dawn and opened the gate. Tian Wen's party got out of the gate and escaped. Tian Wen's policy of treating all his recruits without distinction finally paid off, and a story came down the history.

-End-

Lei-zu嫘祖and the silkworms

Lei-zu嫘祖 was the first Empress of China. (27th century B.C.) . Her name told us that she was an expert waiver. Lei 嫘 means an excellent waiver and zu祖means the originator. She stood by her husband, Yellow Emperor黃帝 fought against their fierce enemy Chi-uo 蚩尤 from the south through defeat eight times and won the final victory with their new invention: Jyy (point) Nan (South) Jen (needle) 指南針. (Compass).

The Yellow Emperor黃帝 was not only a courageous, astute military leader but also a highly efficient administrator. He and Lei-zu with the help of his trusted ministers, ruled wisely and applied Jyy Nan Jen指南針 [2] in many other ways: to navigate the ships, to regulate the field, and to establish the fishing boundaries. The Chinese farming community had extended and progressed in many ways in the last ten years. Now they have written language and advanced medicine knowledge and military means.

Peace and progress Excessive leisure and his subjects' unadulterated worship fed the Yellow Emperor's indulgence of good living. Gradually, the Yellow Emperor enlarged his harem with the beautiful women that his subjugated states sent him as their offerings. He favored particularly the saucy Snow Flake, a petite woman with creamy, fair complexion. Two years ago, Snow Flake bore him a son and the Yellow Emperor doted on both mother and the young prince. Lately, he began to contemplate granting his

---

2   Jyy (point) Nan (South) Jen (needle) 指南針 is the first Chinese compass. The Yellow Emperor invented the compass, which had a needle that pointed to the south. It guided the original settlers in repelling their enemies from the South.

young son the heir apparent instead of his first born, Prince Ein, Lei-zoo's boy.

As a typical submissive wife, Lei-zu was hurt when her husband favored a younger woman, but she took it in stride knowing her own beauty had waned. However, she could not stand for that her son's position of succeeding the throne would be forfeited. Rumors around the royal court had it that the sly Snow Flake frequently marred the Prince Ein's good name with subtle criticisms whenever she could charm the Yellow Emperor. Lei-zu enlisted a few trusted veteran ministers' help. They advised the Yellow Emperor to follow the traditional rule: A virtuous and healthy first male offspring's inalienable right to succeed the throne. Although the Yellow Emperor obviously valued the opinions of his trusted vassals who had fought with him and helped him to build a strong kingdom. Snow Flake's captivating persuasions filled his ears. He dwindled and hesitated to make a final decision.

For a long time the Yellow Emperor absented himself from Lei-zu's quarter and Snow Flake somehow found ways to block Prince Ein's requests of an audience with his father. Out of desperation, Lei-zu wanted to sway the Emperor with her suicide knowing that superstition and the public opinion would make the Emperor honor her dying wish to make Prince Ein, her son, the heir.

On one crispy clear beautiful morning, Lei-zu dragged her feet toward the section of the Yellow River with strong currents. She was a born naturalist and she always loved to observe and utilize the natural resources. Now, even with her heart heavy with indignation and melancholy, she habitually and half-mindedly surveyed her surroundings when she came to the area where the women came to gather the juicy mulberries in the fall.

The rising sun shone on the leaves of the mulberry trees where the caterpillars were feeding or building their enclosed cocoons with the silky thread emitting from their mouths.

Overhead, a few eagles flew through the upper branches of the mulberry tree and shook the wet dew drops on the nearly finished cocoons. The dewdrops bounced off the cocoons, and which showed no signs of being wet. Lei-zu thought, *'that's interesting. The silk threads seem to be very strong and water resistant. Won't it be wonderful to weave the silk thread into cloths and make garments out of it? We never have enough cotton to clad everyone properly.'*

Lei-zu was excited and forgot her suicide attempt. Her new discovery, the silkworms and silk, enabled the Chinese culture leap forward greatly. Of course, her astonishing contribution won her back the Emperor's favor and secured her son's position. Lei-zu discovered silk in Northern China five thousand years ago. It opened the communication and trade between the East and the West. The Emperors of the Han Dynasty of China (206 B.C to 220 B.C.) built the "Silk Route" to improve the commerce with the Roman Empire.

-End-

Cho-di 招弟 had a plan

Lee *Cho-di* 招弟dreamed again that he was eating a bun filled with meat. He refused to wake up but the nagging hunger and his *Lowlow's*姥姥 (maternal grandma) dry cough woke him anyway. Lowlow must feel the hunger more. She always gave him her share of food to eat.

He told *Lowlow*, "Before *Dye* (my father) gets up, I'll go to the forest to shoot some sparrows, and check on the rabbit traps I had set. Hopefully we will have some meat to eat today." *LowLow* whispered, "Be careful, the hungry wolves are out there hunting too."

Cho-di loved his *Lowlow* (maternal grandmother). Actually she was the only grandmother he had. His mother was an only child. As the custom, his orphaned father married the only heir of a small landowner and was considered to be married into his wife's family. Also, according to the custom, his first son would carry his own family name, *Lee* and the second son would carry his wife's family name, *Chen*. His father and his maternal grandpa consulted the only scholar who could read in the village about choosing a name for him when he was born. They named him *Cho-di*. *Cho*招means 'to beckon or to precede' and di 弟means 'younger brother'. They hope that *Cho-di* would have younger brothers.

His father and his grandpa worked very hard and they even managed to save enough money to purchase another lot. Unfortunately, the first disaster came when *Cho-di's* mother died with a stillborn boy when Cho-di was only three years old. Then two years flood followed by severe drought left most of their lots barren. They were poor and Grandpa died two years ago when they had to kill the family cow for food. *Lowlow* said, "His heart is broken."

95

Cho-di's father took him out every day to the forest to hunt to supplement the poor crops they managed to harvest. His father did not want to sell the land and no one could afford to buy land anyway. His father kept on saying, "We have the land. Good years will come."

Cho-di's stepmother often complained that *Lowlow* was a useless old woman doing nothing but eating their meager food, and the ten years old *Cho-di* was lazy and naughty. She was pregnant and she did not want Cho-di, being the oldest son, to inherit the land. She wanted her own son to have the land. Secretly. She plotted to get rid of both *lowlow* and *Cho-di, so s*he forced *Cho-di* to go hunting and foraging at all weathers. *Lowlow* shed tears when *Cho-di* was ordered to go out during a storm with only a sling shot. When his grandma argued that it would be too dangerous for a young boy to go hunting alone, his stepmother ignored her and told her husband that LowLow complained too much. She also said, "We are not rich anymore and we could not afford to pamper him. *Cho-di* gets to learn and be strong." when she sensed that her husband would have said something to keep the boy home.

It was a nice spring with the promising of a good harvest in the fall. *Cho-di* and his father worked very hard to plow the dried-up soil every day. Every night he was too exhausted even to dream. One night, *Lowlow* woke him up and sobbed, "Hush hush, That woman wants to get rid of me. I'm scared."

"*LowLow*, don't cry, Dye (father) won't allow it."

"I'm not his mother. He is soft and he will do everything that woman ask him to do. I overheard …"

"*Lowlow*, you don't hear too well. I don't believe it." *Cho-di* tried to pacify her. Actually, he was very scared. There were stories told times again and again that some folks had abandoned their old ones during a famine.

Next morning after they finished their watered down gruel, his father brought out the old rickety pushcart with an old quilt on it and whispered to *Cho-di* with his eyes lowered, "*Cho-di*, put LowLow on it and took her out to the forest. Left her there. I did not want to do this, but the food is scarce. It's important to keep young one going."

His stepmother pretended crying. She hoped secretly that *Cho-di* would stay with *Lowlow* and she could get rid of them both.

Cho-di obeyed his father as he was supposed to do. He and *Lowlow* both cried and he pushed the cart with *Lowlow* on it toward the forest slowly as he was most reliantly to do it. As soon as they got a little way into the forest, he stated to push the cart as fast as he could and shouted, "*Lowlow*, Hold tight."

He found the big hole in a huge dead tree where he used to hide during a storm and helped his *Lowlow* crawling into it. He said, "*LowLow,* stay here. I'll be back. I hope that I can convince my father and I'll come to take you home. If it does not work, I will be back and I'll be with you. I won't abandon you. Don't cry. I'd better be hurry." He told LowLow his plan and covered the opening with some branches as best as he could.

He pushed the empty cart with the old quilt on it back home fast. His father said to him, "You could have left the cart and the quilt there for her. At least she does not have to sit on the ground."

Cho-di said, "Dye, This old cart is still good. I'll save it. Later, we might have some bad years too and then I can use it to abandon you when you're old and useless. Did'nt you have told me that it's important to keep the young ones going during a famine."

His father looked at him for a long while and then told him, "I have done a bad thing. *Cho-di*, go and get *Lowlow* back. "

Cho-di knelt and said, "Dye, thank you. I would never abandon you." He rushed to the forest and got *Lowlow* home.

-End-

'Cat'猫is not a Chinese Zodiac sign

"**C**ockt doodle do, wake up ..!" one frosty wintry morning when the first pink and gold rays began to show, the Rooster鷄 stretched his neck and sang proudly his daily song. "*Cock doo...*" He stopped abruptly and turned around, talons ready, to face the Cat. He and his hens had to protect their yellow fluffy chicks.

The **Dog**狗 barked and chased the Cat. The Cat jumped on the back of the horse and then up to the roof of the barn.

"*MOO...Quit fighting!*" The **Cow**牛 shouted, "*Cat! You won't get my milk unless you behave!*"

"*Neige... That will be the day.*" the **Horse**馬chuckled softly.

The **Goat** 羊 and the **Pig**猪 sounded their agreements that the Cat was in the wrong. The chickens were family and the Cat should not attack them. They waited and hoped that the Cow could scold the Cat more severely. But they all knew that the Cow and others all liked the cute and naughty Cat.

All the animals that living in and close to the barn respected their leader, the Cow, and the Dog, their protector. They all benefited from the Cow who plowed the field to produce the grain and also her generous supply of milk. It was well known that the Dog would guard the master's properties including them and the barn. Even the Cat knew that the Dog would not really hurt her, a family pet. The **Rabbit**兔, the **Rat**鼠, lived around the barn, were not domestic animals who also counted on the Dog to protect them from predators.

The Rabbit came to the barn with the exciting news. He said, *"My cousin from another warren told me that 老天爺, the Supreme God called all the animals to appear before him. He would then grant special blessings to the first 12 animals who would answer his call to greet him."*

"Moo...We, all of us should go. Our master will let us go. It is winter and we are not busy." the Cow decided.

"I need the God' special blessings. Can I go with you? I dare not go far alone." The Rat pleaded and so did the Rabbit.

"Of course, little ones." the kindhearted Horse said.

"Baa...Be realistic, will you? How could we get up the sky, the heaven?" The Goat questioned.

The Rabbit replied, *"My cousin had overheard the monkeys' chattering. The Supreme God would send down a ladder for the animals to get up the sky"*.

"Where?" The Pig猪 asked, *"Is it far to go?"*.

"At the peak of 泰山, the Mountain Tai."

"Baa...It is not that easy. The God lives on the other side of the wide 天词, Sky River, (the Milky Way). Some of us cannot swim." The Goat said.

"Moo... No problem, they can ride on my back and on the Horse's back." The Cow said.

So they set off and along the way to Mount Tai, the Monkey猴 joined their group.

When they reached the bank of the Sky River, it was decided that the Monkey and The Rooster would go on the Horse's back and the Cow would carry the Rat, the Rabbit and the Cat. The Dog, the Goat, the Pig would swim on their own.

As soon as she got on the back of the Cow, the Cat started to plot. '*Oh good, I sure can catch the Rat or the Rabbit. Oh No, The rabbit is too fast for me, I will catch the Rat. For now, I will wait and the opportunity will surely come.*' The Cat chuckled to herself. She curled up into a ball and faked a nap.

The Rabbit was weary of the Cat also, but he was so sure of his speed and soon relaxed. The Rat stayed alert and prepared to run at any time.

They were on the way and the going was slow. When the Dog swam back to hurry up the lazy Pig, the Cat took her chance and pounced. The Rabbit ran and hopped, with his powerful hind legs, onto the back of the Horse.

The Rat ran as fast as he could, however the Cat had almost caught him.

"*Rat! Get into the Cow's ear!*" the Rooster yelled.

The Rat made a sharp turn and into one of the Cow's ear she went. Hot on her pursuit, the Cat lost her footing and fell into the Sky River. She tried to climb back to the back of the Cow, but the Dog would not allow it. Luckily, they were not far away from the bank and the Cat managed to swim back to it and went back earth dejected. She would not get the God's extra blessings and she needed all her cunning to survive. Later the benevolent God showed her some kindness and granted the Cat nine lives.

Every other animal except the Rat was relaxed after the strenuous crossing. They all knew that they were safe in God's land. So they stopped to feed, to nap or just to enjoy the scenery. The Rat did not relax; instead, he pushed on. He determined to be the first one to get to the God's presence. The Rat reasoned, "*I am sure of that God will grant me extra blessings if I get there first.*" So it was the Rat who became the first one of the 12 Chinese Zodiac animals. God granted the Rat 'a wedding night' on the New Year's Eve.

And so, of all the 12 animals that had traveled to the God's palace became the twelve Chinese zodiac signs. The Rat鼠, Cow牛, Tiger虎, Rabbit兔, Dragon龍 Snake蛇, Horse馬, Goat羊, Monkey猴, Rooster鷄, Dog狗 and Pig猪.

The God named each year after an animal for twelve years. He had set up a system which will help the Chinese people to count and remember the years. Every twelve years would be a cycle, and five cycles totaled sixty years a unit.

It is said that a person may show some of the traits of his/her zodiac animal of his/her birth year.

-End-

狗A dog's low status in China

In China, there are many legends of brave, faithful dogs that fought with wolves to save their masters. Yet the word "dog" in the Chinese language has a condescending meaning. The Chinese don't consider dogs as noble and men's best friends as the way Americans do.

The Chinese have always regarded "dogs" as filthy and lowly species of domestic animals . To the Chinese, a dog's ranking position among the domestic animals is lower than a cow, a horse, a goat. During good years, the Chinese farmers fed their aged and feeble cows or mules and gave them decent burials when they died. A cow or a donkey is eaten as the last food resource only when there was a famine or a draught. The starving farmers would kill the chickens and dogs first. They often said a silent apology or a prayer before they killed a cow for food. They did not feel any remorse when they killed a dog, a cat, or a roaster to eat.

Some Chinese eat dog meat every winter. It's said that dog meat is rich in nutrients and eating it can repel the cold and cure arthritis. To dog meat eaters, the offering of a dish of cooked dog meat to the elders is actually considered a sure sign of piety.

During the Qing (Manchu) dynasty, Master Jing ban-chap鄭板橋 was very fond of dog meat. Was he cruel or insensitive? No. He was a famous painter, a poet, and a benevolent and just magistrate. He just enjoyed eating dog meat during the cold and damp winter. His poems written about a certain dish of delicious dog meat he had tasted with his best friends and his different styles of painting the bamboo branches were equally renowned.

Fortunately, not every dog is edible. There is an old taboo that forbids eating old dogs or young cats. It was said that meat of old dogs and young cats is toxic. It's also said that the meat of the brown dogs might be the best.

Many affluent Chinese in Taiwan have dogs and cats as pets now. The Humane Societies are well established and veterinary science is a profitable and prestigious profession. Chinese dog lovers are as crazy about their pets as Americans are. In addition to feeding, grooming and training, the Chinese dog owners in Taiwan have to guard their dogs from thieves who steal dogs to sell them to the restaurants specialized in dog meat dishes.

Many Chinese sayings fully reflect their traditional low image of the "Dog".狗

1. "A running dog" is a traitor.
2. "A homeless dog" is a downtrodden vagabond.
3. "A dog's fart" is rubbish.
4. "Beneath a dog's shit" refers to the lowest and most immoral behavior.
5. "Worse than being a dog" refers to the most destitute situation when one would prefer death to living.

It is advisable to refrain from calling or comparing Chinese with any mentioning of dogs' noble traits. To the Chinese, being compared to a dog is downright degrading, an insult.

-End-

Three Chinese Poems

All birds sing and all cats mew to call for attention and to express feelings. All men have songs and poems. The Chinese people had songs before they had a unified spoken and written language. Their songs expressed their feelings directly since they are, by tradition, hesitant to express their emotions. Confucius (500 BC) collected and compiled the ancient folksongs into the most popular written language. There are verses of appreciation for nature's beauty chiseled on many rocks at hilltops and lakesides. Poems and lyrical verses represent the mainstream of Chinese literature. The civil examination tested the student's ability to compose prose and poetry. Many poems written by Emperors, prime ministers and generals have been treasured by all. One lesser Emperor (1000 AD) before the Song Dynasty lost his county due to his lack of ability to rule, but his poems expressing his forbidden love affair with his sister-in-law are masterpieces.

Chinese and Japanese (one third of the Japanese characters are Chinese characters) writing words are pictorial, developed from pictures, and sounds. Most characters can be used as a noun or a verb with no tenses. One word has only one sound, and each sound has four intonations. Classical Chinese and Japanese poetry have very strict rules on the number of words in each line, the number of lines and rhymes. For example, haiku, a very short form of Japanese poetry, has a unique formation of three lines.

Unlike modern free verses and surreal poems, most Chinese classical poems were written in one or two stanzas with 4 lines of either 5 words or 7 words. The last word of the 1st, 2nd and the

4th lines must be in perfect rhyme. A poet could ponder the correct word and rhyme for days.

Poem One

This is a poem written by a famous poet in the Yuan Dynasty (Mongol Dynasty, 14th century) with groups of two words. The last line with two groups of three words. I translated it and made every effort to retain its meaning and formation.

枯藤 老樹 昏鴉

小橋 流水 人家

古道 西風 瘦馬

夕陽 西下

斷腸人 在天涯

Knotted branches, Old trees, sleeping crows
Rainbow bridge, Flowing creek, Village huts.
Winding path, west wind, and weary horse.
At dusk, Sun's set.
Lonesome, melancholy traveler, wandering home afar.

Poem Two

This is a typical seven-character poem. 4 lines with 7 words each, written by a poet of the Tang Dynasty (10th century)

少小離家老大回 鄉音無改鬢毛衰

兒童相見不相識 笑問客從何處來

Left hometown young and springy, back home old and sluggish
My hairs grey, beard thin, yet I spoke the village tongue
None of the village teens knew me anymore
They greeted me with a smile, "Mister, where are you from?"

<u>Poem Three</u>

These four lines lyrical verses, written to music, are the first stanza of a masterpiece by a famous female poet of the Song Dynasty. When the Mongolians invaded China, she and her husband were forced apart during the war and she missed him.

君住住長江頭
妾君住長江尾
日日思君不見君
共飲長江水

You, my dear husband, live at the head of the Mighty Yangtze River
And I, your wife, live at the end of the same river.
Every day and every night I miss you, but I can't see you
Although we drink the water from the same river.

It is never easy to translate a poem into a different language. I appreciate your reading of my attempt.

-End-

Section Two

Columns

The Chieftain – Pueblo, Colorado

and

Guidelines – Pueblo, Colorado

Published from 1988-1995

The Archer and the Moon Goddess嫦娥.

Oct 3ʳᵈ (1990) was the Chinese Moon Festival. This is a legend about the Moon Goddess嫦娥.

To all Chinese, the moon is the residence of the beautiful Moon Goddess Chang-O 嫦娥. On the night of the Moon Festival, while eating the moon cakes and admiring the extra bright moon, folks will tell the children the story of Chang-O.

Chang-O's husband, Hou Yih后羿, was a warrior and an expert archer in China about 2000 B.C. One day ten suns appeared in the sky. The earth was scorched and the people suffered. The Emperor, ever mindful of the welfare of the people, commanded Hou Yih后羿 to shoot nine of the ten suns out of the sky. Hou Yih accomplished the herculean task.

Impressed with Hou Yih's bravery, the Goddess of the Western heavens commissioned him to build her a multicolored palace of jade. He finished the difficult job brilliantly. As a reward, the Goddess presented him with an elixir of immortality in the form of a pill.

One day when Hou Yih后羿he was out, his beautiful wife Chang-O嫦娥found where Hou Yih hid the pill swallowed the pill. She found herself airborne, bound for eternal banishment to the moon. Hou Yih set out in pursuit, but was swept back to earth by a typhoon, and he grew old alone.

Another version of the legend is that Chang-O was so breathless on reaching the moon – no wonder, because she had not enough oxygen supply –that she coughed and ejected the pill. Instantly the pill was transformed into a rabbit. Together they lived on the moon forever since the Supreme God made them both immortal.

Even today, colored ceramic rabbits are popular gifts for children during the Moon Festival. When I was a child, I usually collected quite a few each year. Now I don't eat moon cakes or have one Chinese toy rabbit to hold, and the full moon in the United States seems to be different than the moon at home.

The Chieftain, Pueblo, Colo., Sunday, October 14, 1990 Page 3E

A Chinese grandma has 2 birthdays in 1993

A leap year in a solar calendar is the addition of one day in February every four years. In a lunar calendar (known as Chinese calendar), a leap year means the addition of a whole month, 29 or 30 days. It occurs either every three or every five years.

My 95 –year-old mother was born on the 1st day of the 3rd month (lunar calendar) in 1898. According to the lunar calendar, this year is a leap year with a second 3rd month, so my mother had her first birthday on March 24, 1993, and her second birthday will be on April 22 on the calendar used today.

Although she also had two birthdays in 1955 and 1966 and some other years that I don't know about or I don't remember. Her age is the actual member of years of her life plus one. The old tradition is that one would be one year old the day or the hour one's born.

The lunar calendar is based on lunar observation. The interval from new moon to new moon is about 29 and one half days, so a month would be either 29 or 30 days. Twelve months, which totals 354.36 days, form a year, almost 11 days shorter than a year in a solar calendar.

The Chinese lunar year has to be adjusted to the solar year by the addition of one whole month often. The system was established in China around 500 B.C. call for one month to be added on every three years or two months to be added on during a five-year circle. A total of seven months (210 days) must be added every 19 years.

Coincidentally, the ancient Greek lunar Calendar, which was founded about 400 B.C., also added seven months every 19 years.

Except the 1st.9th and 12th months, any of the other nine months can be an additional month during a leap year. The system is very complicated; only the astrologers can decide which year will be the leap year and which month will have the extra one.

I was born on the 1st day of the fourth month and I remembered that I had two birthdays in 1963 in Taiwan. In 1982 I should have had two birthdays also, but I did not know since I forgot to check the dates on the Chinese calendar. It is impossible for me to observe my birthday every year on the same day on the western calendar, since the first day of the fourth month of a lunar calendar could be any day between March 15 and May 15. So I've decided that April 1st is my birthday, but I always try to tell people that I'm not a fool.

The Chinese lunar calendar is widespread in the Far East. The Chinese New Year and other festivals are always simultaneously observed in Japan and Korea.

Page 4F The Chieftain, Pueblo, Colo., Sunday, April 18, 1993

A Miracle of Chinese names

Recognizing one word of a Chinese name and
found distant relatives thousands miles away
from China.

I took my mother to dine at the Mandarin Restaurant in Pueblo,
Colorado. The owner came to greet my 93 years old mother. We
conversed in Chinese. And we found out that Mr. Chang (張先生),
the owner, originally came from the same village where my mother
was born. Consequent discussion led us to the conclusion that we
are very distantly, but definitely, related, even though we had never
met and known each other before. How could we be sure? There
is a logical answer deduced from the traditional Chinese system of
choosing names. In China there are no given names like Nancy or
George. A typical Chinese name consists of two or three one-syllable
words. The first one must be the family name. Then first name will
be one of two ordinary words chosen at random from more than
20,000 existing Chinese characters, separately or together, they
must mean something to reflect the parents' expectation of one's
future. In the past, most middle class Chinese families had their own
genealogical book for choosing and recording names by generation.
A well-versed two-line poem (ten or fourteen words), or a series
of meaningful words would be designated for family members to
derive their mandatory word as part of the name they would name
a child. And this mandatory word would be the key word for a
certain generation. The original poem or phrase or the successive
one, first had to be approved by the elders, then presented it at a

clan meeting, followed by a solemn ritual of acceptance before the ancestral gods. The benefits of this system are to identify a person's position in the family hierarchy and his relationships to others have the same family name from different branches, and also to prevent any possibilities of incestuous marriage. There are fewer than two hundred family names in China; so it is not unusual for a village population over 2000 has only two or three family names such as Lee李, Huang黃or Chan陳.

By recognizing a single word of a name, two strangers having the same family name and meet at a faraway place would know whether they are cousins or uncle-nephew if they knew that they came originally from the same village or the neighboring area.

In this case, the fact is: --The **key word of the generation is in bold.**

My mother's name:

Ting   **Wei** -Shen
丁   惟   慎

Her brother's name:

Ting   **Wei** -Fen
丁   惟   芬

Her nephew's name:

Ting   **Lii** -Yan
丁   履   延

Mr. Chang's aunt's name:

Ting   **Lii** -chien
丁   履   仙

By recognizing the generation word **Lii,** 履**we** know that Mr. Chang's aunt is my mother's niece. That's how Mr. Chang and I know that we are really distantly related.

112

The traditional system of choosing a name indicates that the Chinese society is strongly family oriented. It is sad to see this wonderful tradition, like many others, vanishing, or soon it will be just a thing of the past. At present, most overseas Chinese are likely to adopt Western names for convenience. As the Chinese population spreads around the world, few families will have a family poem, or to have the chance to have a new poem constituted after the existing one is used up. The next generation will have few chances to meet a distant relative even when they live in the same city.

Guidelines Volume 1, Number 3, February 1988 Page 10, Pueblo, Colo.

北京Beijing, Beiping, Peiping, Peking Same city

In Mandarin Chinese, the Chinese official spoken language, *Bei* 北 means north and *Jing* 京 means capital. Beijing 北京 is the northern capital, and Nanjing 南京 (*Nan* means south) is the southern capital. Xian 西安 had an ancient name Xi'jing 西京 (*Xi* means west, or Chang'an 長安 (*Chang* means forever and *a* means security), was the west capital. Incidentally, Tokyo in Japan in Japanese writing and Chinese writing—東京 literally means *Dong* 東*jing*京, the eastern capital.

Kublai Khan, the grandson of the famous Genghis Khan, conquered China in 1271 A.D. and founded the Yuan Dynasty (Mongol Dynasty). He rebuilt and established his capital DaDu 大都 (*Da* means big and *Du* means capital) on the site of the present-day Beijing, a historically military strategic site to the south of the Great Wall, against the perpetual nomad invaders from the north.

It is estimated that the Peking man inhabited Beijing and its surrounding area as early as 500,000 years ago. Written records indicate it has been a political and culture center since approximately 1066 B.C.

Marco Polo visited DaDu (Beijing) and the court of the Yuan Dynasty. The Marco Polo Bridge located just outside of Beijing was built in his memory. On it the Japanese and Chinese had fought hard in World War II.

In 1368 A.D. the Han (the ordinal Chinese people) revolted and overthrew the Mongol Dynasty and founded the Ming Dynasty 明朝. The first emperor of the Ming Dynasty established his capital at Nanjing南京 on the bank of the Yangtze River and DaDu (Beijing)

114

was given the name Beiping北平 (*ping* means peace). His son, the succeeding emperor, moved the capital back to Dadu and changed the name to be Beijing 北京. He constructed and enlarged the palaces, temples in the center and walled it as the Forbidden City.

From 1644 to 1911, Beijing was the capital of the Qing Dynasty (Manchu Dynasty).

In 1911, Dr. Sun Yat-sen and the Republic of China chose Nanning 南京 as the capital and Beijing was changed back to Beiping. Peiping is an earlier Westerner's spelling.

Since Chairman Mao and the People's Republic of China took over the Mainland China in 1949, Beijing has been the capital. Chairman Mao also stopped the use of the old spelling of Peking, reverted it to Beijing. Beijing is more close to the Mandarin pronunciation and also truly reflects the history of this Chinese capital.

Beijing also has an ancient name-Yenjing 燕京. It was the capital of the *Yann* State 燕國 of the Seven States period before the Great wall was completed in 202 B.C.

The Chieftain, Pueblo, Colo., Sunday, October 11, 1992 Page 4F

Bamboo竹 is indeed the staff of life to the Chinese

The lovable Chinese Panda bear lives on bamboo only, and the Chinese people are nearly as dependent on it. Cooking the delicious bamboo shoots, eating it with bamboo chopsticks, and sitting and sleeping on chairs and bed made of bamboo.

Bamboo is a treelike, reed like plant that can grow 100 to 120 feet tall and 8 to 12 inches round in diameter. The Chinese were the first people to discover the varieties of bamboo and its many uses.

Long before the days of Confucius 孔夫子, the Chinese people used bamboo tablets for writing. Such tablets, strung together, became the first Chinese books. And long before the invention of pottery, the Chinese used bamboo vessels; musical instruments made of bamboo were integral to religious rites.

Bamboo also provided the Chinese with their first needles, as well as bows and arrows. About 100 A.D., the Chinese invented paper made of bamboo pulp.

Chopsticks 筷子, writing brushes 筆, fishing poles, brooms, fencing and furniture can be made of Bamboo. The Chinese also use strong, huge bamboos in building boats, bridges and cabins.

Even the leaves of bamboo can be used as wrappings, coverings for hats and roofs. The Chinese eat cooked rice wrapped in bamboo leaves to celebrate the Spring Festival (the 5th day of the 5th month of the Chinese calendar).

Spiritually, bamboo holds special meaning for the Chinese. Its strength and resilience against vigorous wind make the bamboo a symbol of tenacity and uprightness – two highly valued virtues among the Chinese. Together with the pine松 and plum蘭, bamboo 竹 is one of the "three friends三友 of the depth of the winter." For thousands of years, the bamboo has been a favorite subject among Chinese painters.

One high official of the Yuan Dynasty (the Mongol Dynasty) (1206-1368 A.D.) was so fascinated with the ethereal elegance of bamboo that he resigned his post to devote the rest of his life improving his paintings of bamboo.

It is solemnly recorded that scholars classified bamboo one of the four Chun tzu 君子 (perfect gentlemen) of the history of Chinese art. Using the writing brushes 筆made of bamboo, many Chinese scholars and painters write poems and paint pictures showing their admiration of the beauty and the unbending spirit of bamboo. Afterwards, the same poet or painter may enjoy eating a dish or bamboo shoots on a bamboo tray with a pair of bamboo chopsticks.

Truly, bamboo is an inseparable part of Chinese culture and daily living. A famous 11th century poet, Su Tung-po 蘇東波, said, "A man can live without meat, but life would be hard without bamboo 竹."

The Chieftain, Pueblo, Colo., Sunday, July 29, 1990 page 3E

Chopsticks 筷子 Date back to earliest Chinese

Chinese, Korean and Japanese people eat with chopsticks. The most common ones are made from bamboo or wood. Most people cannot afford to purchase the extravagant chopsticks made from ebony or ivory with silver-capped tips, the silver will turn into black or green whenever the food had been tempered with poison. Besides the cost, there is no reason for the lao-bai-xing老百姓 (common folks) to be so over-cautious against poisoning by any political rivals. During the Ming 明 Dynasty (1368-1643 A.D.) and the Qing清 (Manchu) Dynasty (1644-1911 A.D.), assassinations and murders were common among the ruling classes who were constantly engaging in power struggles or political treachery. It is said that many affluent persons carried their own chopsticks, silver-capped of course, to attend banquets. It was not for showing off the wealth or for personal hygiene but a means of self-defense. Just like the Roman Emperor Claudius ordered his servant to taste the food first for safety, the Chinese protected themselves with personal silver-capped chopsticks.

The English word "chopsticks" is not a phonetic translation of the Chinese words "kua tze". According to legend, the Red Emperor's personal element was fire. He is said to have discovered "fire" and cooked food in approximately 6000 B.C.

The Red Emperor also taught his people to pick the hot food with two sticks and this was the beginning of the Chinese chopsticks, Kua tze. Kau means 'quick.' Since using a pair of sticks picking small morsels of hot food from the cooking fire is quicker and safer

118

than using hands, the Chinese people were eating with chopsticks as early as the beginning of Chinese civilization.

One of the early written records of using the ivory chopsticks was in the year of 1100 B.C. The last Emperor of the Shang Dynasty (1766-3677 B.C.) was notorious in his fondness for good food and other luxuries. Kua-tze筷子 rhymed with "quick快son子" and two matching pairs of chopsticks is the important part of a young bride's dowry. Everyone will hope the young couple will eat and live in harmony and give birth to a son soon.

Page 4F The Chieftain, Pueblo, Colo., Sunday, November 29, 1992

Chinese New Year
恭 gone喜shi 發fa 財tsair
Wishing you a happy and
prosperous new year.

The year of the snake (small dragon for the Chinese), year 4588 of the ancient lunar calendar, begins Monday, February 6, 1989. At zero hour on that day, the snake will slither in for a one year reign in the recurring 12 year cycle of mythical (the dragon) wild (the rat, tiger, rabbit, monkey, snake) and domestic (the ox, horse goat, rooster, dog, pig) creatures. The order is: rat, ox, tiger, rabbit, dragon, snake, horse, goat, monkey, rooster, dog, and pig.

It was recorded that the Supreme God 老天爺wants to teach his subjects, the Chinese people, to count and to remember the sequence of years by naming each year with a creature. The smart rat had managed to get there first and the ponderous pig got there last when the Supreme God wants to choose the first 12 creatures answering his summons. Each creature would reign one year.

A thunderous barrage of firecrackers intended to scare evil spirits away and invoke the gods for blessings always punctuates the transition. Many billions people-Chinese, Japanese, Korean- in their native lands or abroad celebrate the Chinese New Year festively with firecrackers and dragon dances.

Similar to the American Thanksgiving celebration, scattered Chinese family members would travel far to go home for their strongly family-oriented New Year holidays. Showing filial respect to their elders and placing memorial offerings at family graves are

120

important aspects of the holiday. The New Year celebration is a grand occasion, the most cherished family reunion.

The lengthy celebration can start from the fifth day before the New Year and last until the fifteenth day afterward—the Lantern Festival on the 15th day of the first month in the lunar calendar.

Of all the numerous activities, the custom of "sending the kitchen God away" was wide spread. On the third evening before the New Year, every household would burn the old and greasy portrait of the Kitchen God (火神祝融), officially known as Duke Chang. The folks would first offer the departure kitchen God some very sweet and sticky cakes. The kitchen God had watched over the family against fire and bad luck for a whole year, and now is the time for reporting the family members' behavior to his boss, the Supreme God in heaven.

The sweet and stick cakes should sweeten up his heart so he would relay only the good deed, at the same time hoping his hips will be too sticky to go into the details of any wrongdoings. The Kitchen God will be back at midnight on the New Year eve when the folks would post a new portrait of him over the stove and he will resume his duty for the following year.

During the festival days of the merrymakings and feasts, most parents would restrain from quarreling between themselves or scolding the children. Naturally the children enjoy the good wish money and the freedom of being mischievous and eating.

The Chieftain, Pueblo, Colo., Sunday, February 5, 1989

Chinese keep in touch with ancestors at graves

I n Taiwan (the Republic of China), a spring Memorial Day has been officially established on April 5.

Literally, it's called "掃墓節Sweep the Grave Festival" or "Tomb Sweeping Day." Coincidentally, the late Generalissimo Chiang Kai-shek died on April 5, 1975. The observance of this special day has become a mixture of official and private affairs in Taiwan.

The Chinese are noted for their family-oriented society. A Chinese would be expected to be pious to his elders while they are alive and show respect to their graves on the Sweep the Grave Festival and other holidays.

On the other hand, the Chinese people are very practical. They want their dead elders to be able to live comfortably underground. On April 4, the folks in Taiwan will visit, clean, fix and beautify their relatives' graves before they reported in details of their achievements or sufferings to their spirits. They will reverently burn paper-made articles of clothing and furniture, gold or silver nuggets (as money) as offerings to the dead and hope that their ancestors will not suffer poverty in the world of spirits. Finally, they will leave plentiful delicacies for their ancestors to have a feast with neighboring lonesome spirits.

Nowadays, the majority of the Chinese is no longer overly superstitious, but keeps up the tradition and place flowers there showing their respect and feelings for the dead.

After a dreary winter, the Tomb Sweeping Day is also a joyous occasion for showing off bright colored new outfits. Everyone, young and old, enjoys a picnic with games and flying kites if the weather permits. Under the presumably watchful eyes of their dead loved ones, everyone must be cheerful lest the ghost should worry.

Before I left Taiwan in the '70s, I, a teacher at that time, and other civil service workers had the privilege of going home two hours earlier than usual on that April 5. Since my family had moved from North China, we only had a symbolic service at home to commemorate our ancestors' tombs in Shantung, North China.

My father and one of my brothers died in Taiwan while I was abroad. Sadly, I was unable to attend their funerals and I had not been able to visit their graves even once.

On the eve of this Chinese Spring Memorial Day, I pray for their blessings and support. I wish to draw the needed courage for facing the unknown future from remembering them and also to please my 95 years old mother who is living with me at Pueblo West. Colorado.

The Chieftain, Pueblo, Colorado, Sunday, April 5, 1992 page 3E

Children in China get bunnies too—in the fall

"Why are they selling the "Lord Bunny兔爺爺" in the spring? My mother asked me after seeing the Easter Bunnies on sale in a store at Pueblo Mall. "These are not "Lord Bunnies", they are Easter Bunnies," I told her. In Northern China where I was born, the children will get toy rabbits made of clay and eat moon cakes during the Mid-Autumn Festival (The Moon Festival). The toy rabbits are hollow inside. On the outside, there are beautifully painted picture of a distinguished looking gentleman with a long beard. The ones made in Beijing are most extravagant, with court costume and white-soled boots. This is another legend about the rabbit resided on the moon. According to the legend, there was a righteous Minister Chou who tried in vain to give sound advice to a tyrant about 12th century B.C. ago in China. The tyrant ignored his advice and sent him to prison. From the dungeon he continued sounding his criticism. The mad tyrant killed Chou's son and force Chou to eat his son's flesh before banishing him. Saddened by the death of his son, Minister Chou retched. His vomit turned into a white rabbit and flew to the moon and became a god-in-residence there. It is said that, on a clear night, one can see a figure of a rabbit under a tree on the full moon.

On the day before the Moon Festival in 1948, the year before my family left Shandong, North China, for Taiwan, I went to school feeling very sad. In the preparation of the move, my mother dismissed my nanny, who was the one who reminded my mother about buying me a "Lord Bunny" every fall. That year I did not have even a cheap plain one. I remembered that I held my head high and smiled all day until my jaw hurt and kept saying, "I don't want one. It's silly." In Taiwan there are no "lord Bunny" since it is a custom of Northern China.

The Chieftain, Pueblo, Colo., Sunday, April 12, 1992 page 3E

Compass指南車

Columbus' compass was ancient 'magic'

The magnetic compass was the first one of the famous four inventions of the Chinese. The other three were paper, wood-block printings and gunpowder.

The Yellow Emperor was the legendary and mystical first political leader of the Chinese farming state along the Yellow River (黃河). He invented a chariot equipped with a magic needle pointed to the south, where his enemy was. It was called Chih-nan-ch'e指南車 (point south chariot.).

About 2500 B.C., the Chinese people were in war with their violent southern neighbors. The Chinese had more advanced weapons and chariots and more soldiers, but they were defeated again and again. Their southern enemy could conjure up dusty storms to make the Chinese lost their senses of directions.

It was recorded that the Yellow Emperor led his people fight nine battles with the southerners and defeated eight times. On the eve of the ninth battle, a god came to his dream and showed him the magic way of a floating needle that point to south and north.

Yellow Emperor built a special chariot to carry the magic needle and directed his army accordingly. With the full confidence knowing where the enemy was, the Chinese did not get lost again and won the war.

During the Sung Dynasty (960-1279 A.D.), the Chinese began using the compass in their ocean-going junks. The Arab and the Mongolian carried the compass to Europe in the 12th Century and it played an important part in the great voyages of discovery by Europeans mariners.

In 1492, nearly 36 centuries after the compass was first invented, it helped guide Columbus on his voyage of discovery to America.

The Chieftain, Pueblo, Colo., Sunday, October 14, 1991. Page 4A

China had its own version of King Solomon

Here is the story of how a Chinese magistrate of the Sung Dynasty (circa the 12th century) reunited a baby boy to his birth mother.

A wealthy family of two brothers lived harmoniously in a town south of the present day Shanghai. The two wives shared the supervision of the servants peacefully and the matriarch praised her two daughters-in-law often.

A year later, nearby neighbors heard nothing but the voices of three young women yelling and arguing over a crying infant. The elder brother's wife claimed that she gave birth to a healthy baby boy and insisted that she, not the wet nurse, hold the baby herself. But the younger brother's wife said that her sister-in-law, with the wet nurse's help, stole her baby immediately after she had a difficult delivery.

The well-to do mistresses wore fashionably loose and layered garments and were waited on hand and foot, so both of them were plump from good living. It was difficult to tell whether one was pregnant or not. Whether the husbands knew about their own wife's pregnancy or not was a difficult issue in itself.

Traditionally, only the firstborn male offspring would inherit the family wealth: it was doubtful that the husband of the fraud woman was not in on the plot. So, the two wives and one wet nurse fought with words and the two brothers fought with fists. The servants either joined the fight or took the opportunity to be lazy or even thieving. The elders of the clan could not solve the case and finally the matter was brought to Magistrate Wang's court.

Magistrate Wang ordered a huge circle to be drawn on the hard earthen courtyard and then had the infant put in the center. He ordered, "Lao Tien yea老天爺 (the almighty God of the sky) will be the judge. Hear! You two women! God will help the real mother. Whoever takes the baby out of the circle first will have the baby!" Before Wang finished his order, the two women rushed into the circle and started to fight over the baby. The poor baby cried from pain. Hearing the baby's wailing, the younger brother's wife stopped pulling lest they would harm the infant, while the elder one doubled her effort and pulled harder. She triumphantly held the baby and shouted to her weeping sister-in-law, "The baby is mine."

"You are not the baby's real mother. You are greedy and cruel. I'll have you to be jailed for two years, "Magistrate Wang declared with authority, "The real mother wouldn't hurt her own child!" So saying, he handed the infant to the grateful younger brother's wife.

King Solomon's Chinese counterpart wisely solved a family matter with a different twist.

The Chieftain, Pueblo, Colo., Sunday, September 1994. Page 4F

Chinese opera a stylized art form Steeped in culture

Chinese opera is a combination of dances, songs, dialogues and pantomime performed on a simple stage of only a table and two chairs. Sitting on one side of the stage behind a portable screen are three or four musicians who play gongs, cymbals, and an oboe. An oboe is a violin like musical instrument with only two strings.

The music, which sounds bizarre to the Western ear, blends well with the characters' voice and dance. Different tones announce the appearance of a high-ranked personage, a young woman, an old woman, or a person arriving in a hurry. However, there is no music whenever there is a dialogue or monologue.

The plots are uncomplicated and easy to follow, mostly are drawn from popular novels, historical events, folklore and mythology. An actor may walk to the front and address the audience directly with a monologue to identify himself, to explain a situation while the other characters on stage are not supposed to hear what he is saying. Meanwhile, the theater aides can rearrange the table and chairs, or an actor can signal his valet to bring him his personal long-necked teakettle for him to take a sip if he is wearing a long beard.

There is no attempt to simulate reality in the stage properties. Pantomime, the movement of the finger tip, the hands and the dance with the wide sleeves are all parts of the acting. Pushing ahead and apart with hands combining with an exaggerated step forward is sufficient to show the opening of a gate and entering. Walking with a certain way and holding a stick is enough to show a man on a horse.

Emperor Chen Tsung of the Song Dynasty (1000 A.D.) edited and unified various folk plays and created the Chinese opera as it is today. Most costumes are based on those worn during the Tang Dynasty. (600-900 A.D.) There are different colors, headgears, masks and makeup to indicate the rank and status as well as the personality of the characters in the play. A good person of high rank will wear green; the Emperor, yellow; a very old or very young man, white. A wicked person will wear a white mask; a faithful general will wear a black or red mask.

A complete story will take at least three hours to perform. Before the 20th century, male actors had to play the female roles since the foot-binding custom prevented ordinary women from enduring a long period of singing, standing or performing an elaborate dance. Nowadays, an accomplished actress can play a male role.

It will take years for a player to learn how to sing and talk with the high-pitched voice, and to remember the standard lines, the sophisticated ways to point a finger or wave the long sleeve. Most actors or actresses begin training at a young age and specialized at playing one kind of character,

On the other hand, the standard performance enables the theatergoers to follow or anticipate the plot and action easily. They are familiar with the plots and enjoy seeing how different players portray the same roles.

Chinese opera is popular wherever there are Chinese. Many traveling troupes take this art to the villages and remote areas.

The Chieftain, Pueblo, Colo., Sunday, Mar12, 1995 Page 8E

Confucius' birthday

September 28, 1992
2543rd anniversary of Confucius' birth

Confucius was born on the equivalent of September. 28 in the year 551 B.C.

His real name was Kung Chiu孔丘 (Kung is his surname and Chiu, his given name, means hill). Later he was respectfully called Kung Fu-tze 孔夫子 (the grand teacher Kung), Con-fu-cius is the popular English translation.

The Chinese government in Taiwan officially observes September 28, as "Teachers Day", all teachers and students will have a day off for celebration.

Ceremonies commemorating the birth of "The Sage and the Grand Teacher of all generations" would be held at all Confucian Temples. The minister of the interior, representing the president of the Republic *c* of China, and the mayor of Taipei will attend the birthday rites at the sacred Confucius Temple in Taipei. They would wear the formal traditional Chinese attire-a long blue gown and a long sleeved black jacket.

At the end of a troubled period called the "Spring and Autumn" when China was divided into many warring states, Confucius was born at Qiefu in the present-day

Shandong Province. Confucius was an inspector of corn markets for the state of Lu before he devoted his mission as a teacher. With his 3000 pupils, He wandered about, from court to court, attempting to convince the rulers of the right way to govern. He could not convince his immediate contemporaries with his high standards of humanity and virtues and he died a disappointed man at seventy-two.

Confucius originated a philosophy of life, which had a formative influence on the culture of China and much of the Far East. Confucianism, the name given to his teachings, is not a religion but a code of conduct and a guide to morality and sincerity in both personal life and public conduct. Every emperor of every dynasties of China would officially visit Confucius Temple and home in Shandong, North China.

He once said, "One should revere the gods and the ghosts, but still keep them distant." On the other hand, he participated in ritual activities because he considered ritual and music are important. He believed ritual would keep man in order and music would unite individuals and bring joy.

His disciples collected the sage's sayings in "Analects of Confucius". Here are a few elected well-studied verses:

"What you do not wish for yourself, do not do unto others."

"All men of the world are brothers." "

"Choose a job you love, and you will never have to work a day in your life."

"It does not matter how slowly you go so long as you do not stop."

"I hear and I forget. I see and I remember. I do and I understand."

The Chieftain, Pueblo, Colo., Sunday, September 27, 1992. Page 3E

Confucius owed much to His lovely mother.

Confucius was born in the year 551 B.C. His real name was Kung Chiu孔丘. He was respectfully called Con-fu-cius 孔夫子 (The great teacher). His father died when he was three years old, his mother had raised him alone.

Confucius' father was an ugly and tall warrior with Herculean strength. Once he stood and held up a heavy gate barrier long enough for his king and his follow warriors to escape out of the city. It was the enemy's trap. He had several daughters and one son, who were crippled from a deadly disease (probably polio). His wife died soon afterward.

Knowing that Mr. En had five unmarried daughters, Confucius' father went to visit Mr. En with a marriage proposal and indicated specifically that no dowry would be needed. Mr. En then asked his daughters about it and the four elder ones all refused to be married to an old and ugly giant. Jen-ze, the youngest and prettiest daughter answered, "Piety and obedience are two important virtues. I'll obey my parents' order if you want me to marry Mr. Kung." She knew that her parents had financial difficulties to prepare five sets of dowries. That is how Confucius' father came to marry a pretty young girl.

Jen-ze was a good wife but had no children for a long time. She and her husband prayed to the God of Mountain Chiu and were granted a son. Legend has it that when the pregnant Jen-ze walked uphill in the late fall, all the dried grass turned green and all the dead wild flowers bloomed again. It is also told that her bedroom smelled fragrant and pleasant during the time of delivery. These were the divine indications that Jen-ze will give birth to a sage. With her dedicated care and love, her son Kung Chiu grew up to be the greatest teacher and world-famous Confucius.

The Chieftain, Pueblo, Colo., Sunday, May 23, 1993 Page 3F

The celebrations of Christmas – Chinese-style

J esuits introduced Roman Catholicism to the Far East – China, Japan – as early as 1550. The first Jesuit mission in China was founded in Beijing, capital of the Ming Dynasty, in 1582.

There are many cathedrals and churches in China today, and Chinese Catholics and Protestants all observe and celebrate Christmas. There are even some villages whose residents are all Catholics, and they celebrate Christmas every year in the traditional way.

In Taiwan, Christianity also prospered. The late Generalissimo and Madam Chiang Kai-shek, both are devoted Christians. They advocated and fostered religious liberty.

The Christmas celebration is a sanctified observance for true Christians in Taiwan. The younger, westernized generations see Christmas as an opportunity for parties and dancing all night long. Christmas trees and exchanging gifts are fashionable and popular.

December 25 is also a national holiday for the Chinese in Taiwan. It is the Constitution Day, and it is the historically significant memorial to the "Xi'an Incident" of December 25, 1936.

After Dr. Sun Yat-sen overthrew the Qing Dynasty and founded the Republic of China in 1911, many strong warlords fighting among each other. China was divided. Later, in his effort to establish a "united front" against the invading Japanese and to build China as a republic based on the Constitution advocated by the late Dr. Sun, Chiang Kai-shek negotiated and warred with many strong-headed warlords. On December 4, 1936, while conferring with one of these powerful warlords at a historically famous hot springs resort 12 miles north of Xi'an (the famous west capital of the First Emperor who built the Great Wall in 202 B.C.), Chiang Kai-shek was captured and held hostage by the warlord who hoped to gain political advantages.

Madam Chiang (Soong Mei-ling), the daughter of an American-trained Chinese preacher and the first Chinese Bible publishing, was American-educated and a Christian. She alerted the nation and the world about her husband's imprisonment from Shanghai. Under the pressure of an indignant public, the warlord released Chiang Kai-shek, agreed to a ceasefire and joined the constitutional government.

The date of Chiang Kai-shek's release happened to be December 25, 1936. Later some Christians said that Madam Chiang prayed and "The Lord answered her."

Thus, December 25, Christmas Day, became 'Constitution Day' in Taiwan. The Chinese are glad to have a day off from the five-and-a-half day workweek to enjoy a festival.

The Chieftain, Pueblo, Colo., Sunday, December 25, 1988 page 3E

Dragon Boat Festival honors poet

The Chinese refer to the Dragon Boat festival or Spring Festival as the Double Fifth because it falls on the fifth day of the fifth month of the lunar calendar. This will correspond to June 5th in 1992.

It is one of the three major annual festivals among Chinese. The other two are the Lunar New Year and the Moon Festival.

Legend associated the Dragon Boat Festival with the death of a famous poet-statesman, Chu Yuan屈原, in 299 B.C. Chu Yuan was an incorruptible minister who drowned himself in the Milo River of present-day Hunan province, south of the Yangtze River. His contemporary common people respected him for his loyalty and integrity. On hearing of his suicide, they rushed out in boats to search for him. Unable to find him, they threw cooked rice into the river to feed the fish and crabs so that Chu Yuan's body would be intact. That was the begging of the traditional 'Dragon Boat Race.'

Besides the exciting Dragon Boat races, the main feature of the traditional commemoration of the anniversary of Chu Yuan's death, the Chinese will eat Tsung-tze粽子cooked rice wrapped in bamboo leaves. Last week, my sister sent me some dried bamboo leaves and a bag of sweet rice (glutinous rice) so that I could cook Tsung-tze for my mother.

In Taiwan, This festival is also observed as 'Poet's Day,' since Chu Yuan was a famous poet. There are many poem writing contests as well as poem-reading parties.

With the Dragon Boat Festival, the Chinese welcome the summer and look to the dragon to ensure enough rain for a good harvest. Since there will be more insects in the summer, thus spreading diseases, the children will wear Hsiang-Pao, the small and colorful perfumed sachets filled with insect repellent on this holiday. Some girls will present their hand-embroidered Hsiang-Pao (small pouch) to their boyfriends to convey feelings they are too shy to express in words.

Chinese also drink **Realgar wine** 雄黃酒 (a Chinese alcoholic and medicated drink) to repel the insects and be immune to the diseases from the insects bites.

The Chieftain, Pueblo, Colo., Sunday, May 31, 1992 page 3E

First Chinese tyrant ruled in the 17th Century B.C.

Five thousand years ago, The Chinese civilization blossomed along the Yellow River to the north and the rich delta areas of the Yangtze River to the south. During the reign of the Emperor Shun舜 (2255 B.B. to 2205 B.C.), the Yellow River 黃河 flooded seriously. The Emperor ordered Yu禹, a chieftain of the satellite state Xia夏 to control the flood.

It took Yu thirteen years to accomplish the Herculean task of changing the course of the Yellow River. In 2205 B.C. Emperor Shun passed the throne to Yu, since Shun himself was chosen a successor by the preceding Emperor Yao.

Instead of carrying on the merit system of choosing a new emperor, Yu handed the throne to his direct line and established the Xia夏Dynasty, which ruled China for more than 400 years.

In 1819 B. C., Yu's 14th descendent Emperor Jia 桀 was the first tyrant recorded in the Chinese history. Jia the Terrible ruled 54 years. In 1786 B.C., with his imperial army, he conquered and captured the chieftain of Shang商State in the present day Shandong province. In order to gain the whole tribe's survival, Shang offered the beautiful Cher喜 (meaning joy) to be one of Jia's royal consorts. Contrary to her name, Cher喜 (Joy) hardly ever smiled and was nothing but happy in her state of slavery to a cruel dictator, even though her exceptional beauty monopolized Emperor Jia's favor. Emperor Jia would try anything to make her laugh and she only laughed when she heard the sound of expensive silk and satin tearing.

In her way of revenge, she enticed Emperor Jia into excessive drinking and pleasure seeking. Jia built a big pond filled with expensive wine and stacked the banks with delicacies and held parties all night long.

Jia ignored the suffering and poverty of his people and the counseling form his good ministers. His prime minister warned him that the people would revolt if he did not amend. Jia replied, "Nonsense, I will be the emperor as long as there is a sun." Hearing this, his people lamented and pleaded, "Sun God, please perish and we'd rather all perish together than live and suffer"

It is said that Jia also built a huge hallowed post of copper for torture. He would order the rebels to be tied to the post to be burned to death slowly while a fire was burning inside the copper tube. One righteous minister protested and Jia ordered him to be roasted too.

Finally, all the subordinate tribes united and revolted. The new leader established the Shang Dynasty in 1766 B.C.

The Chieftain, Pueblo, Colo., Sunday, November 8, 1992. Page 4F

General Ge went fishing for a wise chieftain

In 1122 B.C., 90-year-old General Ge Zhi-Ya 姜子牙 commended the united army of 800 small Chinese tribes and they overthrew the tyrannical Emperor Cho 紂, the last emperor of the Shang Dynasty. General Ge assisted his young Lord to establish a new dynasty, Zhou 周朝 with two capitals. The central administration was located at Xi'jing 西京 (western capital), the present day Xi'an 西安. This became a most important strategic military site since the ancestors of Genghis Khan (the Mongols) threatened the Chinese from the west.

Under Ge's advice, the first emperor of Zhou 周朝 also rebuilt the ruined capital of the Shang Dynasty, Luoyang 洛陽, as a secondary capital.

Ge was born at Luoyang. According to the legend, Ge studied Taoism 道 somewhere in the Himalaya Mountains until he was 70 years old. His shi-fu 師父 (teacher with a father's authority) sent Ge home because he predicted that only Ge, predestinated by the supreme god, could save the Chinese from chaos. Without any money and having lost all contact with his family, Ge came back to his hometown and married a 68-year-old maid. With his in-laws' help, Ge tried many trades in vain. It seemed that misfortune followed him everywhere. One anecdote states that once, when Ge looked up and pleaded with the Tian 天 (sky, meaning God), bird droppings fell into his open mouth. Ge left his complaining wife and went to the west alone. More reliable folklore has it that his in-laws chased

142

him away. Anyway, the destitute Ge姜子牙, now in his 80s, became a bona fide vagabond.

One day, when Ge went fishing at the bank of the River Wei 魏 just outside of Xi'an, he was so absented minded that he either lost the hook or simply forgot it. A distinguished gentleman asked him why he fished that way. Ge, judge from the attire that this man must be someone important, answered wittily that he wasn't fishing for fish but for a great chieftain who could appreciate his talent in military and political affairs.

That was how Ge met the father of the first emperor of Zhou 周朝, and together they succeeded in establishing a strong Zhou Dynasty周朝 (1066-221 B.C.)

The Chieftain, Pueblo, Colo., Sunday, March 28, 1993. P.4F

Helen of Troy contemporary corrupted the Chinese court

When the Trojan War was being fought over the beautiful Helen in the 12th century B. C., 800 small Chinese tribes united and overthrew the tyrannical Chou紂, the last emperor of the Shang Dynasty, who had been bewitched by the notorious but beautiful Dar-jii妲已.

According to the legend, Emperor Chou was clever and gifted with Herculean strength. He could outrun and kill a tiger with his bare hands, and he also could grab the tails of nine bulls and pull them with one hand. He and his virtuous queen ruled adequately until he favored Dar-jii. It was told that an evil spirit of a fox ate the innocent girl's soul and possessed her body on the real Dan-jii's long journey to the capital. Emperor Zhou was totally under the evil girl's spell at the first sight.

Shortly after she gained Emperor Zhou's full attention, she plotted and killed the queen so she became the queen. Gradually she started coercing the emperor to employ whoever gave her gifts and demoted the ones who were righteous. Soon the court became corrupted.

Emperor Zhou and Dar-jii lived in luxury while the people suffered. The royal couple started using chopsticks made from ivory imported mostly from the India and built grand palaces with man-made lakes and forests. Sometimes, the royal couple would hunt for months and the royal chariots ruined the crops.

The subordinate tribes rebelled. Emperor Chou was captured and killed and new dynasty, Zhou周, replaced the Shang Dynasty.

144

Dar-jii did not want to die together with Emperor Chou as the custom dictated. She wanted to bewitch the new ruler and be his queen again. The primary advisor and general of the new regime was the legendary Ge Zhi-ya 姜子牙 who was in his 90s. He wisely beheaded Dar-jii before his young emperor saw her.

It was said that the tearful Dar-jii charmed and softened the soldiers' hearts and no one could raise the knife to execute her. Even the old General Ge had to order her enchanted face be covered before he, himself, could kill her.

Helen of Troy's beauty is famous throughout Western history and Dar-jii's wickedness, more than her beauty, survived Chinese history since the male-oriented society and historians could easily blame a woman for the downfall of a dynasty.

The Chieftain, Pueblo, Colo., Sunday, February 7, 1993 Page 4F

How moon cakes defeated the Mongol Dynasty

T he eighth month of the lunar calendar is the month of the harvest. On the 15th day, the moon is full, the Chinese (and many other Orientals) will celebrate the Moon Festival (or the mid-autumn festival. 中秋節)

In 2011, this important Chinese festival will be on September 12th. The Chinese will worship the moon goddess—the beautiful Chang-O, 嫦娥, and thank her for a bountiful year or ask her blessings for a difficult one.

The Chinese will also enjoy eating moon cakes月餅. These are pastries, round to resemble the shape of the moon and filled with anything from sweetened red bean paste to delightfully sticky fruit slices, meat and nuts. In the United States, one can purchase boxes of moon cakes from stores in any Chinatown.

Legend surrounding the moon cakes placed the origin of the traditional delicacy in Han Dynasty (200 B.C.). At the end of the Yuan (the Mongol) Dynasty (1206-1368 A.D.), the **'moon cakes'** played a major role in the Chinese natives' rebellion, led by Chu Yuan-chang, successfully threw off the Mongol yoke and restored the monarchy to Chinese. Genghis Kahn conquered and ruled China in A.D. 1206. He admired the Chinese culture very much. He named his dynasty Yuan元 (means commencement), ordered the Mongol to study Chinese language and observe Chinese customs.

,Chu *Yuan-chang* and his Chinese resistance group distributed thousands and thousands of 'moon cakes' to the Chinese only in

Beijing and asked them to eat the cakes at a specific divine (holy and lucky) hour on the night of the moon festival.

Slips of paper placed in the moon cakes contained a call to arms against the Mongol invaders living among the Chinese. The surprised revolt succeeded.

The Mongols ended their 160 years occupation of China, and the legend of the 'Moon Cakes' lived forever among the Chinese.

The Chieftain, Pueblo, Colo., Sunday, September 30, 1990 page 3E
Revision – September 7, 2011, Boston, Massachusetts.

In China, Use care lest you ask for a horse

Five thousand years ago, the Chinese people observed that the sun is round and radiating strong white light, so they draw a picture representing the sun, and likewise another picture representing the moon.

The picture of the sun ⊙ the word of the sun 日

The picture of the moon θ the word of the moon 月

And that's the beginning of the pictorial Chinese written words. Later they modified the rounded form into square characters composed of straight, horizontal or vertical lines and dots, and each character retains more or less the symbolic form of the original picture. Each word is monosyllabic.

Because there is no alphabet, and the Mandarin (the dialect of Beijing and the official Chinese spoken language) has only about 400 vocal sounds, the pronunciation cannot be logically traced out, so each character must be memorized.

The Chinese children study hard in the first, the second and the third grade. There they learned the basics, with pointed fingers tracing the strokes while speaking aloud one character at a time. They have written assignments every day. They write each word hundred and hundred times.

In comparison with many other languages, including English, Chinese speakers use fewer vocal sounds. In English, "to, two, and too" sounds the same. But in Chinese, each sound usually is assigned hundreds different written characters that carry unrelated meanings. The sound MA, for example, can be many different written characters with different meanings: mother, hemp, horse, and ant, scolding…It are distinguished by four intonations, or pitch of tones:

MA (even tone) 馬

MA (rising tone) 蔴

MA (dipping tone) 媽

MA (falling tone) 罵

The written characters for the meanings of MA demonstrate a unique phenomenon – the phonetic loan process- of the Chinese language. Originally, the pictograph for horse was pronounced MA. Gradually, this character was adopted for other words pronounced MA, and written beside other character radicals (roots) that indicate meaning.

Written besides woman 女 means mother 媽

Written under two mouths 口口 means 罵

When speaking Chinese, a person must be careful with the four intonations, or he could find himself in trouble.

To buy買 is pronounced mai, with a dipping or curved tone, and to sell 賣is also pronounced mai but with a falling tone. If one cannot distinguish the different tones, he could be misunderstood. Once a western priest told his servant to buy him a piece of hemp 蔴 (ma-rising tone) but did not say it in the right tone. His servant bought him a horse 馬 (ma-dipping tone) instead.

Although there is only one form of written Chinese languages, not everyone in China speaks Chinese the same way. There are many dialects deviating from the standard Mandarin speakers, and the mastery of the written form will take at least a year of daily practice. It is worth the effort, because the knowledge of the Chinese language will open the doors to the Orient.

Page 4A The Chieftain, Pueblo, CO. Friday, November 11, 1988
Pueblo West Eagle, Volume 6, Issue 6, June 1991
Published Monthly

In China, the written language has kept the Chinese united

C hung Kao 中國 ("The Middle Country") is the way the Chinese named their country because they thought that China was located in the center of the universe. For thousands of years, China shared and spread her unique culture among her neighboring countries; Japan, Korea and Vietnam... Their ideographic or pictographic written language then became widespread over Asia.

In the 9th century A.D., the Japanese appropriated Chinese characters to write their own language, which sounds different from the spoken Chinese but retains the meanings of each character.

Today a Chinese person can partially understand the written Japanese language even if he cannot speak Japanese. A lot of the Japanese characters are actually Chinese characters. Before they have their own languages, Koreans and Vietnamese borrow heavily from the Chinese too, especially for literary writing.

The Chinese characters were invented almost 5000 years ago by observing the shapes, the sounds of the animals and the environment around them.

Pictures: **Sun ⊙ Moon θ Water 〈〈〈**
Written words: Sun 日 Moon 月 Water 水

The written language was first developed along the farming communities striding the Yellow River, the present Henan and Shandong provinces. The vast territory and many mountains and rivers caused isolation. There were different forms of written Chinese words and many different dialects. In 202 B.C. Chin Shi Hwang

秦始皇, The First Emperor, conquered six warring states after 400 years of constant wars and established a strong Chin (秦) Dynasty. He built the first Great Wall, a canal that connected the Yellow River and the Yangtze River, highways crisscrossing the country, and completed the unification of various and slightly different versions of the pictorial Chinese written characters. From then on, even though the Chinese speak different dialects and sometimes could not understand each other, they all shared the same written language, Han. This strong force keeps the numerous Chinese a united nation.

There are hundreds of different dialects and all are monosyllabic. Mandarin of the north, Cantonese of the South and Shanghaiese are the most-spoken tongues. Mandarin is the native tongue for Beijing, which has been the capital of China for nearly 800 years. All of the Northern provinces' dialects are similar to Mandarin. Thus Mandarin was the court language of the past and is now the official language of China. Movie companies in China, Hong Kong and Taiwan all hire the best Mandarin speakers they can find for their films. In the United States, most of the emigrants from China during 1940 and 1960 were Cantonese. Later a lot of others (speaking Mandarin or Shanghaiese) and Taiwanese (speaking Taiwanese) arrived in the States.

It is quite common for two Chinese persons meeting abroad to communicate in English because they speak different dialects. However, they all might be literally well versed in Han漢, the Chinese written language.

The Chieftain, Pueblo, Colo., Sunday, September 25, 1988 page 3E

151

In China, the name tells about the person

L ong before Confucius 孔夫子 was born, the Chinese established a farming social system centered on family and clan.

Family fame and achievements, not the individuals, has always been sought and treasured. To emphasize the unity and importance of the family, the Chinese people adopted a unique naming system, which is designed to trace the family "root", as well as establishing a clear-cut family hierarchy.

In China, there are fewer than 200 family names – originally the names of tribes. Today in mainland China, it is not unusual to find a village populated by 3000 people sharing two or three family names; most of them are one-syllable words such as Chin 陳 or Lee 李, and occasionally there are two words, such as Oh Young歐陽.

There are no given names such Amanda or Joseph. A typical Chinese name consists of two or three one-syllable words. The first one must be the family name, followed by one or two ordinary words chosen from more than 20,000 existing Chinese characters, separately or together will mean something. For example, my name is Yu Shiao-shen于孝慎 Yu 于 is my family name, 孝 Shiao means (piety) and shen 慎 (means prudence.) The three-word name must sound pleasing with an upward tilt, and appears balanced when it is written. My sisters' names are: 于孝淑, 于孝恭 and于孝端.

The Chinese believe that a person's name can influence his entire life. It is vitally important to have a good, auspicious name which not only reflects the parents' expectation but also their good wishes and blessings.

152

In the past, most middle-class families had their own genealogical book for choosing and recording names by generation. A well-versed, two-line poem of 10 or 14 words or a series of meaningful words would be designated for family members to derive their mandatory second (or third) name word, and this mandatory word would be the key for a certain generation.

The original and the successive poems, which were chosen by the family and approved by the elders, then presented at a clan meeting, followed by a solemn ritual of acceptance before the ancestral gods.

The benefits of this system are to identify a person's position in the family hierarchy and his relationships to other with the same family name from different branches. It also provides a means for tracing the family root. By recognizing a single word (the generation word), two strangers have the same family name and meeting at a faraway place will know whether they are related, providing they know that they came originally from the same region.

Here are examples of Chinese names, with the mandatory generation word in boldface.

Mao Test Tung 毛澤東: 澤 **Tse** (lake) and 東 Tung (East, sun will rise). His family name is 毛

毛澤健 Mao **Tse** Jiann : 健 Jiann (means important) is his first cousin.

The late president of the Republic of China (Taiwan) was:

Chiang Jing **Gwo** 蔣經國. jing (means to manage) and 國 **Gwo** (means states/kingdom.) His brother, Chiang Wei **Gwo**蔣衛國.

The Chinese naming system fully reveals that the concept of "family as a unit" is the very strength of the Chinese society and culture. Non-Chinese groups, the Mongol and Manchu, conquered China but eventually were absorbed into the Chinese. Thus any doctrine that contradicts with the Chinese concept of family will not be able to prevail for long.

Marxist communism has not worked well in Mainland China. The new Chinese chieftains are leading China to a reformed communism more in line with the Chinese tradition, and a fast developing China is emerging.

In Taiwan, The government has successfully combined the Western influences with the Chinese tradition, and Taiwan is quite advanced in every way.

The Chieftain, Pueblo, Colo., Sunday, June 5, 1988, page 3E

In China, things can be confusing when Chinese converse

Cantonese, Shanghaiese and Taiwanese are all Chinese. They have the same culture, history, heritage and written language and Mandarin is the official spoken language. However, they speak different dialects. As a result, in the course of conversation, misunderstanding and confusion often occur.

Here are a couple of humorous stories that I heard while I was visiting New York and I'd like to share with anyone who is interested in things Chinese.

A customer at a Chinese restaurant was a Cantonese, asked the Taiwanese waiter for a piece of fried banana topped with syrup for desert. He asked "*Iee-* (one) *gen* 根 (piece) of banana."

He waited for quite a while. Finally the waiter showed up with a platter of fried bananas and said apologetically, "Sorry, you have to wait so long. I had to go out to buy more bananas." The waiter had misunderstood the customer and thought that he had ordered one *Jin* 斤 (approximately 1.3 pounds) of banana instead of just one *Gen* 根 (piece) based on the customer's Cantonese pronunciation. In the Taiwanese dialect, *Iee Gen* 一斤 means a lot of bananas.

Of course, the single customer could not eat all the bananas and was furious about the expense. They argued.

The proprietor humorously solves the dilemma by asking other guests to share the banana treat. Everyone shared a big laugh when the proprietor wrote a poster and hung it on the wall.

"*Iee Gen* 一根 is not *Iee Jin* 一斤. If in doubt, write it." He said, "We Chinese speak many tongues. Luckily, we have only one written language." Another guest said, "Thanks to The First Emperor who established one written language two thousand years ago."

***

After the end of the Second World War, the Soviet Union had captured and had kept **Pu Yi** 溥儀, the Last Emperor of the Qing (Manchu) Dynasty in captivity in Siberia for five years. In 1950, The Russians handed him back to the new Chinese government-The Communist China. Pu Yi, the last Emperor, was assigned prisoner number 981 and the Communist Party tried to "reform" him with other political prisoners.

One day a jail guard, a Northern (Shandong) soldier called aloud, "Prisoner 九八么 *Yeu* (Northern Chinese slang for 'one' and sounds same as 'wanted'). Before the tall and slow moving Pu Yi (Last Emperor) could respond, a short and dark Shanghaiese prisoner rushed forward and answered, "Here I am." in his anxiety to please the jailor and to avoid an impending punishment if he could not respond fast enough. He was number 98 and he had heard "*Joe* 九 (nine) *Ba* 八 (eight) Wanted."

After the confusion settled, this incident created a rare chance for the harsh guards and the scared prisoners to share a laugh.

Even though the Chinese speak many different dialects, they have only one written language that had united them.

The Chieftain, Pueblo, Colo., Sunday, September 1, 1991 page 3E

The legacy of two wives' tears.

The Yellow Emperor was the legendary and mystical first political leader of the Chinese farming state along the Yellow River (黃河). About 2500 B.C., Yellow Emperor and his people were in a lengthy war with their southern neighbors.

The Supreme God (老天爺) inspired the Yellow Emperor to build a chariot with a compass, called指南車 (point south chariot.) With it, he led his people to a final victory. His territory expanded, culture and commerce flourished. The Empress discovered silkworms. The pictorial Chinese writings and the Chinese medicine were also developed.

By then the Chinese civilization was blossoming along the Yellow River to the north and the rich delta areas of 長江 (Long River, another name is Yangtze River) to the south. According to the legend, the Yellow Emperor was the successor of the Red Emperor, whose patron element was fire and the color red. The earth, colored yellow, was the Yellow Emperor's patron element. The Yellow Emperor reigned from 2697 B.C. to 2595 B.C. His direct descendants succeeded him and the capital was located at a town in today's Shanxi Province, not far from the present day Xi'an (西安).

The Emperor Yao堯, the great great grandson of the Yellow Emperor was historically renowned for his wisdom and fairness. Instead of passing the throne to his son, he selected his son-in-law, Shuen 舜 to be his successor in 2255 B.C.

Emperor Shuen ruled China wisely was a strong advocate of piety. He lived almost to the age of 100. Near the end of his reign, the Yellow River flooded extensively. Following the preceding emperor's example, he passed the throne to his able minister Yu

157

禹who strategically changed the course of the Yellow River and stopped the nine-year-long flood.

For some reason never clearly explained in Chinese history, Emperor Shuen and his two wives, two daughters of Emperor Yao, left the north and moved to the south. He died in 2208 B.C. and his two wives cried day and night. Their tears stained the bamboo growing along the Xiang River湘江 in today's Hunan province.

The mottled bamboo is called Xiang-fee 湘妃 (妃means empress or royal consort) grows mostly in southern China. Throughout Chinese history, many poems lamenting the two sisters have been written.

The Chieftain, Pueblo, Colo., Sunday, January 19, 1992. Page 3E

孟子 *Mencius' mother moved thrice*

To the world, Confucius is the famous sage of China. To the Chinese, however, Mencius孟子, a renowned follower and advocate of Confucianism, holds the equal if not greater esteemed position as the number 2 sage throughout their history.

It is believed that the wisdom of Mencius' mother contributed a great deal to his success.

Mencius was born in 372 B.C. in a village close to the frequently flooded Yellow River in northern China. Shortly after his birth, there was a flood, Mencius' father, a scholar, put his wife and their newborn baby in a big wooden bathtub, himself was drowned.

The baby and mother survived after being carried by the current a long way downstream. This is how Mencius came to grow up in the province of Shandong where Confucius was born 175 years earlier.

The first home, where Mencius mother managed to earn a living as a wash woman, was in the neighborhood of butchers. Watching her young son playing games of handling carcasses, she decided to move because she hoped that her son would be a scholar. Unfortunately, the second home she moved to was also a wrong choice because pretty soon Mencius began to imitate the neighboring bricklayers.

Enlightened by the fact that the youngster would learn easily by imitation, she moved the third time to an area where quite a few scholars resided. She worked as a weaver in the home of Mr. Kung, a teacher and Confucius great grandson.

There was no money to buy expensive writing materials. Bamboo or silk strips were used as paper at that time. The inexpensive paper wouldn't have been invented for another five hundred years. Mencius mother encouraged her son to practice writing on the sandy beach. He could use his finger first and later willow twigs to trace the complicated strokes of the Chinese characters on the sandy and learn the Chinese words.

One day the adolescent Mencius told his mother that he did not want to study any more. His mother realized that her repeated coaxing and advice were ineffectual. So, she cut a piece of nearly finished tapestry off the loom and told the startled boy by example that his quitting learning now would be just like cutting the tapestry before its completion.

"My son, you would never be a scholar and this segment of tapestry would never be a useful product," she said. Awed by his mother's demonstration, Mencius studied hard and became a famous educator and philosopher.

The Chieftain, Pueblo, Colo., Sunday, May 10, 1992 page 3.

New portraits of kitchen god go up this week

The year of the roaster, the year 4592 of the Chinese calendar, will begin soon in 1993. Chinese families in Taiwan and in mainland China are busily shopping around for a new portrait of the kitchen god.

Traditionally, on the third evening before the Chinese New Year, every household will burn the old and greasy portrait of the kitchen god "Tsou Shen" (or Duke Chang, the god of the stove) after offering him some very sweet and sticky cakes.

The kitchen god had watched over the family against fire and bad luck for a whole year, and it's the time for him to report in details the family members' behavior to his boss, the supreme god in heaven. The sweet and sticky cakes should soften (sweeten) up his heart so he should only relay the good deeds. At the same time, people hope his lips will be too sticky to go into details of any wrongdoings of theirs. Then at midnight, a new portrait of him will be posted on the wall in front the hearth, and he will resume his duty for another year.

The worshipping of the deity of a stove (fire) is an ancient custom. It was mentioned in the Analects of Confucius and other old writings about how he Chinese held sacred ceremonies and presenting offerings to the god of the stove and fire.

During the Han Dynasty, a careful noble man had the habit to bless (to inspect and to prevent kitchen fires) the stove before dawn every day. A few days before the New Year, he had a vision of the kitchen god and made the proper offerings to the god. From then on, the Chinese have worshipped the kitchen god every day, and have a new portrait of the kitchen on the wall shortly before the New Year celebration.

According the legend, the kitchen god, Mr. Chang Tan, was a righteous man with a delicate face. He was also very careful about preventing the spreading of fire from cooking. He, with the help and six daughters, busily warned the folks about the dangers of kitchen fires and had extinguished a few when he was alive. (Circa 1400 B. C.). The supreme god ordained him to be the kitchen god.

Some families will post two portraits, Duke Chang and his wife. The offerings to the kitchen god can be extravagant or simple, but the "fire preventing" and "blessing" are important.

In 1947, the last time my family had the offerings to the kitchen god in Shandong Province, North China, I ate too much of the sweet cakes and suffered a terrible stomachache. My nanny comforted me and held her hand over my mouth so that I could not cry loud lest the departing kitchen god would hear me. I will always treasure this memory.

The Chieftain, Pueblo, Colo., Sunday, January 17, 1993 page 3E

October is the month for Chinese history

O ctober is the busiest month in Chinese history. It's the month of many important observances, both on Mainland China and in Taiwan.

October 1st is National Day of the People's Republic of China (mainland China). On October 1, 1949, Communist Chairman Mao Tse-tung declared the birth of the P.R.O.C.-People's Republic of China in Beijing's Tiananmen Square after his total victory over Chiang Kai-shek's government. Chiang Kai-shek moved to Taiwan, the folks in Taiwan do not celebrate October 1st.

For R.O.C Republic of China-Taiwan. October 10th is "Double Ten National Day"- the 10th day of the 10th month. It was on October. 10, 1911, Dr. Sun Yet-sen and his revolutionary army successfully overthrew the Qing Dynasty (Manchu Dynasty) and proclaimed the birth of the Republic of China. On October 10, 2011, folks in Taiwan celebrated in style the 100th birthday of Republic China. 1911 was the first year of the new Republic of China.

October 21st is Overseas Chinese Day. It is not an official holiday.

October 25th is Taiwan Retrocession Day. On October 25, 1945, the 34th year of the Republic of China, the defeated Japanese officially return Taiwan to China. Taiwan was lost to China in 1985 when the Qing Dynasty was defeated by Japan. Every year the Chinese in Taiwan celebrate this memorial anniversary of the termination of 50 years of Japanese occupation.

October 25th, 690 A.D. was a significant date in Chinese history. On that day (the ninth day of the ninth month of the lunar calendar),

163

Madame Wu, the 67-year-old dowager of the Tang Dynasty, officially declared herself "Empress" of her own government, the Chou Dynasty. She demoted her son, the Emperor of the Tang Dynasty. She was the first woman totalitarian in Chinese history and she ruled China 23 years.

October 31st is Chiang-Kai-shek's birthday. It is observed as Veterans Day in Taiwan, while it is ignored completely by the folks in Mainland China, the communist China.

The Chieftain, Pueblo, Colo., Sunday, October 28, 1990 Page 2E

Personal chop圖章: Don't leave home without it

The Chinese do not honor written signatures. Instead, personal chops are used on bank deposits, licenses and other legal documents. Now in 2018, as far as I know, one will still need his/her 圖章**for banking and other business transaction.**

A personal chop (stamp) is a small block or hard-surfaced material with an individual's name (two or three Chinese characters) sculptured inverted and reversed on one end. It can be oval or round but the most commonly used are square. Inked with some red-paste-like substance, a Chinese can stamp his name right side up on papers as binding endorsement.

Instead of a line for written signatures, a Chinese document will have a designated square for the personal chop. An artist will stamp his personal chop on his paintings. One can find a stamp, the painter's, on every Chinese or Japanese paintings, just like one would expect to see Raphael's signature on each of his masterpieces.

A personal chop can be made from an inexpensive wood block with a person's name simply sculptured just for a practical purpose. Every summer when thousands of students register for the highly competitive college entrance examinations on Taiwan, chop-makers will produce and sell the waiting students, dirt cheap, personal chops made hastily from a block o hard soap. It will be used once only.

A permanent chop usually will have the person's name intricately and artistically sculpture on extravagant ox-horns, ivory, rare rocks or exquisitely colored hard plastics. It comes with or without a matching box with built-in ink well.

Every chop is produced by hand, one character at a time. Even if the same chop-maker produces two identical shaped chops for the same person, they will still be different. Since every Chinese must have a personal chop, the chop making becomes an independent branch of arts as well as an occupation developed and improved with a long history.

Everyone can have more than one personal chop; it is up to the owner to remember which one is being used for what purpose. Mr. Lee can open a savings account and a checking account in the same bank with two different chops. He or a servant can withdraw money from his savings account only by presenting the same chop used when he opened the account.

The bank teller will check and compare the registered chop card on a file every transaction n just like an American bank teller will check against the depositor's signature-card. Without that particular chop, Mr. Lee himself can't withdraw money regardless of how sweetly he may talk or how hard he may argue.

If one loses his chop, he must announce the annulment of his chop by an advertisement in the newspaper for three consecutive days and register a new chop with the bank right away. In Taipei, Taiwan, there are small newspapers that will do business prosperously in publishing exclusive "loss of chop" notices.

And on almost every busy street corner in any city, there will be a chop-maker working busily while the customer is waiting. Americans can't leave home without identification and Chinese can't leave home without identification and one or two personal chops.

The Chieftain, Pueblo, Colorado, Sunday, July 1, 1990 page 3E

Proverbs provide subtle guidance

C hinese proverbs are some of the everyday speech that represent wisdom and truth. By quoting a suitable proverb, A Chinese can give advice subtly or save an argument among friends.

A thoughtful Chinese person would not say, "Think before you speak." Instead he would say, "Think three times before you'll do it."

Confucius' teachings advocate that subtle advice is more effective than blunt rebuke. "Should" is a strong word which is used only sparingly by a father or a teacher. Since a direct reproof would often arouse the listener's resentments or even rebellious retorts or behavior.

A lot of Chinese proverbs refer to meals 飯. "Fan" 飯 means cooked rice or, by extension, any cooked grain and it's the main part of an everyday Chinese meal. Proverbs derived from "rice 米" are both practical and readily understood by all.

A few proverbs associated with the word rice 米:

"Even a clever daughter-in-law can't cook without rice" --means that without the right material and tools, even the greatest skill is useless.

"Every lady strikes the edge of the rice pot once in a while." --means that even the best of the family will have disagreement sometimes.

"The rice has been cooked."-- means that the past or the fact cannot be changed.

"Drawing pictures of rice cakes won't stop hunger." --means if one really wants something, one must work hard for it.

"If you eat his/her rice, you must obey him/her." --means whether one likes it or not, one must take orders from the boss.

Shiao Shen Yu 于孝慎

There are some humorous sayings utilizing the word "fan" too. For example, a person who is a lazy or good for nothing is called "*fan* □ *ton*, a cooked rice pail," since he accomplished nothing but ate.

"*Fried cold or leftover rice.*" Is a sarcastic expression saying that a writer or a speaker is merely recycling a previous work or a speech.

These proverbs and humorous expressions have been handed down from the generations of the past, and I hope the children of the overseas Chinese will understand and preserve them.

The Chieftain, Pueblo, Colo., Sunday, September 6, 1992 page 3E
Pueblo West Eagle, Volume 6, Issue 11, November 1991.
Published Monthly

R.O.C.中華民國--Taiwan
P.R.O.C.中華人民共合國--
Mainland China

The year of 1949 will live forever among the Chinese. The civil war between the Nationalist Party (Kuomintang 國民黨) and the Communist Party (共產黨) had started even when they superficially united in the eight years long Sino-Japanese War. Chinese and Japanese had been in war four years before the Japanese attacked Pearl Harbor and the World War II started.

In 1945, The Japanese surrendered. Chinese were overwhelmingly thrilled with the victory. However, at the same time, the civil war was intensified when the Soviet Union fully supported the Chinese Communist Party, while the Nationalist Chiang Kai-shek's military forces were equipped with newer U.S. weapons and airplanes.

But the Chinese Nationalist soldiers had no heart to fight and to kill their own countrymen. "老天爺 (The Supreme God) forbids that we war on our own brothers and neighbors." In 1949, The Nationalist government escaped to Taiwan. Only the presence of the United States Navy's 7th Fleet in the Taiwan Strait keep the victorious Communist leader Mao Tze-tung and his huge army from overtaking Taiwan.

For a long time, Taiwan and Mainland China had been hostile to each other. Each one schemed and strove in vain in the effort to defeat the other and to unite the whole China.

Taiwan (free capitalists) and Mainland China (Communists) are two political entities that bear different names.

169

Taiwan is the Republic of China R.O.C. 中華民國. The name was established in 1911 when Dr. Sun Yat-sen 孫中山 overthrew the Qing (Manchu) Dynasty on Oct. 10, 1911. The new government announced that the year 1911 would be the 1st year of the Republic of China 中華民國 -Taiwan. Since traditional and throughout the history of China, every new emperor would adopt a prosperous name for his reign and started a new count of the year when he was crowned. The Last Emperor of the Qing Dynasty, Pu Yi, **and** 溥儀 announced 1908 as the first years of his reign. Oct. 10th is "Double Ten National Day" for the government in Taiwan. On October 10, 2011, the Chinese in Taiwan will celebrate the 100th National Holiday.

Mainland China is the People's Republic of China P.R. O.C. 中華入民共合國. This name was established on Oct. 1, 1949 when Chairman Mao 毛 came into power. They appropriated the western count of years for their new government. The National Day is October 1st. October 1st, 2011 will be celebrated as the 62nd National Holiday in Mainland China.

The Chieftain, Pueblo, CO. Sunday, January 27, 1991 page 3E
New version – Sept. 6, 2011, Boston, Massachusetts.

Rat weddings 老鼠結婚

On the third night of the lunar New Year, Taiwanese will observe a unique custom of "Rat weddings." Among the twelve animals that responded to the Supreme God's call of meeting, the Rat was the first one got there. She deserved to be the first symbol in the Chinese zodiac. According to a Taiwanese legend, the benevolent God also reserved the third night of the New Year to be the rats' wedding night and let them be multiplied. On that night, folks in Taiwan will go to bed early, putting out the lanterns or turning off the lights lest the mice's matrimony processions be disturbed. Some thoughtful families will also spread rice, corn and other tidbits of food in the corners for the mice to enjoy. It's their way to share their prosperity and also to please the Supreme God while asking for another fruitful year.

On the other hand, some folks will claim that the reason for the earlier darkness in the house is to prevent the mice's wedding from proceeding smoothly. They believe that the mice cannot see well in the dark and there will be less time before dawn for the newlyweds to produce offspring.

Two different approaches of the same custom fully reflect how the kind farmers, most of them are Buddhist; adhere to the principle of not killing the mice and their dislike of the idea of having more of them. The practical side of this custom is to prevent fire, lest the tired folks become careless after two days and nights of feasting and merrymaking.

The Chieftain, Pueblo, Colo., Sunday, January 29, 1995 page 6E

Rocks gave rise to legends

Here are three famous Chinese rock stories.

The first one: 'Three Laughs Rock' at the foot of Tai Mountain, Shandong Province, North China.

Legend has it that three centenarians always met for a game of chess or tea on the top of this big rock. One day they were talking about their secrets for living a long life. The first one said, "I always take a leisurely walk of a hundred paces after meals." The second one said, "My secret is that I never eat until I am full. I will stop eating when I am still a bit hungry." The third old man only grinned and said nothing. After being asked twice, he finally said, "Me? My secret is that my ugly wife keeps me from enjoying too much sex." The three of them roared with laughter and the sound of their laughs echoed in the mountains for three days. Later some one carved the words 'Three Laugh Rock' on the rock. It is said that tourists can still see a faint trace of the words on the rock today.

The second one: 'The Stubborn rocks who Nodded.'

During the South and North divided period (circa 6th century A.D.), Buddhism became popular and widespread in China. One famous monk, Tin Chu Master, arrived at the Tiger Mountain near Shoo Chou City, north of Shanghai. He gathered a group of rocks at the foothill and started to preach the doctrines of Buddha to the rocks. When he came to explain some intricate ideas, he asked the rocks, "Do you understand?" and all the rocks nodded. Later some scholars use this story as an analogy: If one uses simple terms to explain a difficult matter, even simpletons can understand.

The third rock: "Three lives Rock" in the beautiful West Lakes area near Hon-Chou City, south of Shanghai.

There was a rock known as "Three Lives" in the famous Tinchu Temple which was build in memory of the monk with the same name. legend has it that during the Ton Dynasty (9th century A.D.), a monk and a famous scholar met at the site of the rock and became good friends. When they had to part, the monk said, "After my death, please come back here at the site of this rock twelve years later, we'll renew our friendship." Scholar Lee was sad when he heard that the monk had passed away. He kept his promise and return to the rock twelve years later. There he met a young shepherd. The shepherd was the monk's reincarnation and they were good friends again. The moral of this story is that true friendship will last forever.

The Chieftain, Pueblo, Colo., Sunday, August 15, 1993 Page 4F

Spirits return for "Chinese Halloween"

The seventh month of the lunar calendar is the month of the ghosts鬼. The Chinese (and the Japanese) have a month-long Halloween. Any festival day observed according to the Lunar Calendar will vary from year to year in relation to the Gregorian calendar. In 1990, the seventh month of the lunar calendar will begin on August 20.

The Gate of Hades (黃泉 Yellow Spring) would open for the spirits to return to earth for a month-long visit. In demonstrating their filial respect to their deceased family members, many traditional activities will be observed during this month of the ghosts.

The 13th day of the seventh moth is the day reserved for the ghosts of the family. The living family members will burn incense and spread delicacies to welcome them. For the farewell, folks will burn paper-made articles of clothing and furniture, gold or silver nuggets (for money)...for the spirits to enjoy and to live comfortably underground later.

The biggest occasion of the month falls on the 15th day. It is said that on that night, all kinds of ghosts including the homeless and the ones who died violently or accidentally without being properly buried will roam freely on earth. Food and other offerings will be spread on the roadside or on the street corners for the homeless ghosts. Hopefully, they will be satisfied and pacified and they will not rob the docile and content ghosts who had just received good offerings from their family members.

174

Water lanterns (Shi Deng, floating paper lanterns) will be floating on near-by creeks or rivers. For the inland area, the paper lanterns will be put on a shallow basin of water. Besides being a symbol of the floating nature of the spirits, the lanterns also serve the purpose of illuminating the ways (of blessings) for the wandering souls.

For a whole month the ghosts move freely among the living and it's said there are mischievous ghosts who may play a trick or two. Some folks insist that their household articles will disappear and reappear mysteriously.

There are superstitious taboos that might be observed during the month of the ghosts. The most common one is that it is not a good time to move or to marry. In addition, the folks are advised to be more cautious about fire.

Anyway, the seventh month is the hottest and the driest month in most provinces in China. It's really too hot to prepare a wedding or to move.

The Chieftain, Pueblo, Colo., Sunday, August 12, 1990 Page 2E

Student demonstration
學生示威游行

On May 4 1989, thousands of Chinese university students in Beijing marched to Tian Anmen Square (天安門), Beijing, China. They demanded freedom and democracy in politics, speech and publication, the freedom we take for granted in the United States.

On May 4, 1919, devotees of Dr. Sun Yat-sen shouted and protested the old and unfair social and political situation at the same location in Beijing. Mao Tze-tung was then a student and librarian at Beijing University. China joined the winning Allied Forces in World War I. On April 30, 1919, Versailles Treaty determined that Japan, not China, would take control of Shandong province in northern China from the defeated Germans. The Chinese were astonished and angered by this unfair settlement. Students and workers protested everywhere.

On May 4, 1919, approximately 3000 university students in Beijing organized the demonstration and the whole country joined in. Beginning as a political demonstration, it turned in to the movement of continuous demand for reform. The importance of education, the abolishment of foot-binding ordeals of women, the eradication of opium became the priorities of the new cultural movement.

What started in 1919 shaped and influenced the modern Chinese ideas today. Hopefully this new student's demonstration will lead China to be a truly free and democratic country.

The Chieftain, Pueblo, Colo., Sunday, May 1989. Page 3E

To be 'old'老 in China is to be honored

It is an honor to be called '**old**' in China.

Respect for the old is one of the most essential social values established early among the Chinese. In a predominantly family-oriented society, the 'aged' elders always hold prominent positions in the Chinese families. Gradually, the word '*lao*'老 (old) had transformed into the meaning of respect.

When the word *lao*老 (old) precedes any title, it has a way of elevating the importance of the position. For example, the word *shih* 師 itself means teacher. And *lao* Shih 老師 (old teacher, literally) actually means 'respected teacher'. A young Chinese teacher will automatically be called *lao shih* even if he is actually only in his 20s.

There is another Chinese word, *tzu* 子, when means child, sage, saint or a very wise and learned man. This word could be applied together or interchangeably with *lao* (not old but respected) when referring to an honorable personage. The founder of Taoism was called Lao-tzu 老子 because he was a very old man with unfathomable wisdom. His real name was Lee Uer 李耳. Lee was his family name or surname and Uer was his given name, which means ear or listening.

His teaching of Tao 道, the natural way, has become famous and widespread since 600 B.C. Following another social custom of refraining from mentioning one's esteemed elder's name openly, his followers respectfully called him Lao-tzu老子 (an old wise man).

His title, Lao-tzu, has since come down in the history and his real name, Lee Uer was only known through books and records.

177

Confucius was once Lao-tzu's student. Likewise Confucius's real name, Con-chiu 孔丘, was obliterated from popularity, and only his honorable title, Confucius孔夫子, meaning a wise, old teacher with the surname Con 孔 has carried throughout the years and gained world-wide recognition. Today, if a young man in China is called 'old friend' or 'old brother', he does not feel offended. Instead, he feels honored.

The Chieftain, Pueblo, Colo., Sunday, January 27, 1991 page 3E

Two Eastern myths about the Milky Way

The seventh day of the seventh month of the lunar calendar has special meanings to Chinese, Japanese and other Asians. When it is a clear night, the stars Vega and Altair shine brightly in the night sky. Millions of Chinese and Japanese people would look up the Milky Way and reminisce the touching legends about these two stars.

The Japanese version:

It is an ancient legend. A boy of 15 and a girl of 12 had wed and lived happily ever after into old age. They were so close that one could not live without the other. After they passed away in each other's arms, the merciful gods raised them up in the heaven together as the girl star Vega and the boy star Altair, who now dwell on opposite banks of the Milky Way. Many Japanese couples will ask their blessings of marital happiness.

The Chinese version:

Legend has it that a guilty but beautiful lesser goddess in heaven had been punished and thrown down to the Earth for seven years. She fell in love and married a young farmer. The supreme god granted her petition to stay on Earth, but his wife, a cruel but powerful goddess, threatened to kill the husband and a son if she would not returned to the heaven immediately. The poor girl flew skyward when her family was sleeping. But the husband woke up, carried their son on the back of his faithful cow and started to chase after her. Responding to his pitiful pleading, the supreme god

179

sent many thousands of birds to carry them to the sky. The angry Goddess, wife of the supreme God created a wide river, the Milky Way. The birds failed to carry the husband and his son across it.

That is how the girl star Maiden (Chinese name for Vega) and the boy star Cowboy (Chinese name for Altair) stay forever on the opposite banks of the Milky Way.

It is said that numerous birds will build a bridge with their wings for the two stars to meet on the eve of the seventh day of the seventh lunar month. In 1993, the seventh day of the seventh month was August 24. Even though their legends are different, Chinese and Japanese all observe this custom annually.

The Chieftain, Pueblo, Colo., Sunday, October 3, 1993 page 4F

What is the Chinese religion?

Taoism, Buddhism, and Confucianism: which one is the Chinese religion? What does the average Chinese believe? Besides the numerous Catholics and Protestants and the many devoted Buddhists, the majorities of the Chinese people choose none of these three as a personal religion but nevertheless believe and follow the teachings of every one of them. Even a lot of Chinese Christians cannot completely rid themselves of the influence of Taoism, Buddhism, and especially Confucianism.

Before the year 221 B.C. Confucius established a system of morality and logic. He taught that the people should examine themselves to discover their desires, and that man should rely on his own power of reason. This moral system took over the function of a religion in Chinese society.

Gradually Buddhism, which migrated from India, Taoism and other traditional beliefs were added to the Confucian system. The mixture is the philosophy or the ideal code of conduct of the Chinese people. Throughout history, scholars have studied this philosophy diligently.

However, in daily life, spirit worship and rituals are very popular. There are many temples honor all the gods, saints of both Taoism and Buddhism. Everyone can go to a temple to worship a certain deity of either religions, and to pray for protection or ask for blessings. For instance, a woman can walk into a Buddhist temple and ask the Kuanyin, a Buddhist goddess, to grant her a male child. In a different court of the same temple, she can also worship Lao-tzu, the founder of Taoism, and ask his help in winning a game of mahjong. Many historical figures also become objects of worship and hold distinctive places in temples. Their spirits are believed to exist eternally, and they can be called on for help.

In addition to Confucius, other historical figures that are now revered by many devoted worshipers in Taiwan are Guan Kung, an extremely loyal and brave general of The Three Kingdoms periods (200 A.D.), and Mat-su, a legendary goddess of the sea who saved a lot of shipwrecked sailors and fishermen.

In Taiwan, freedom of religion and beliefs is fully guaranteed. Cathedrals, churches and temples stand side by side, and all rational religious beliefs are respected.

Traditional Chinese beliefs and the religions of foreign origins all work harmoniously to promote their teachings.

The Chieftain, Pueblo, Colo., Sunday, November 25, 1990 page 3E

Wind, water 風水 (fung shui)-- Chinese Geomancy

The art of determining lucky sites of Dwellings, Graves and Gardens Similar to the mysterious European way of using a "Dowsing Rod" in finding water underground, the Chinese adopted a system of geomancy for finding and determining the choice (Lucky) sites for houses, graves, and even gardens since time immemorial. There are a lot of writings about the manner in which a building or a burial place must be laid out in order to afford the most perfect compliance with the principles of YIN 陰 (moon/shadow) and YANG 陽 (sun/light), and not to disturb the Earth Dragon. The earliest recorded dated about 200 B.C., the same period when the Great Wall was first built. The first Emperor who built the Great Wall applied 風水 **(fung Shui)** to find the site of his burial ground. Later during the Song Dynasty (960 -1127 A.D.), the practice of 風水 (fung Shui) became very popular.

The scope of 風水 (fung Shui)-geomancy, presents a wild field of study. It constitutes divination based on the extension of the underground watercourses, the presence and location of the hills in the vicinity, and other geographic detail as well as the avoidance of evil atmosphere. Traditionally, the profession of 風水 Geomancer, just like the Chinese medical doctors, was exclusive family enterprises. The skills, the instruments used, the secret knowledge, were all considered guarded family legacies which would only be handed down from father to sons (not daughters.) The instrument used is a geomantic compass, a disk with written symbols: 陰陽 (yin and

183

yang) and the five elements: metal, wood, water, fire and earth all around and a compass needle in its center.

A 風水 master would probe the ground with his special compass first and then chose a good site for his client. He would scoop up a handful soil and observed its color (dark red is the best) and its texture (dry is better than overly moisten) and then let the soil drop freely to the ground so that he could examine carefully the pattern it made. He would have to make sure the building (or the grave) site would not be a swamp, and at the same time having stuffiest draft and moisture. The building should not be built on the eyeballs or on the neck of the Earth Dragon, since the irritation of the sleeping dragon would be disastrous.

Next, he would decide which the direction the gate should be opened to, so that it will be impossible for evil demons to sneak up and into the house. The gate/door facing East, South and West would be better than facing North, and the left side of the building should be slightly higher than the right side, the back side should be slightly higher than the front.

A perfectly chosen or a naturally good 風水 site or sites will not only benefit the dwellers of the building, or the descendents of the deceased buried in the grave. It will also uplift the development of the surrounding area. I think the Pueblo, Colorado with the mountains to the west, rich farm lands in the east, and the Arkansas River flowing through …must be a naturally very good 風水 site.

Guidelines, Pueblo Edition, Volume 1, Number 5, April 1988 Page 9, Pueblo, Colo.

酒Wine has a long history in China

Wine drinking has caused many historical perils in China. Emperor Yu of the Xia Dynasty (4116 – 2205 B.C.) enjoyed the taste of wine often during his 13 years battle with the vagarious Yellow River. However, he warned his son to be aware of the corruption and evil that the indulgence of wine would cause. In 1766 B.C., Emperor Yu's 17th descendant, Emperor Jye, drank excessively and lost the throne. Six hundred years later (1122 B.C.), Emperor Chou the Terrible also ended the glorious Shang Dynasty as the result of excessive drinking.

On a positive note, there are many historical records of wine drinking as an important means of diplomatic negotiations. Frequently, potential battles had been avoided when two conflicting leaders dissolved their animosities over lengthy drinking and open, relaxed discussion.

Wine also inspires the flourishing of excellent artistry. The famous poets of the Tan Dynasty (618-905 A.D.): Li-Bai李白, Tu-Fu杜甫 and Wang-Wei王维, the lady poet Li Chin-jaw: 李清照 of the Song dynasty and other famous artists delivered their masterpieces when they were drunk and being nicely intoxicated.

Unlike the English language, there is only one Chinese character for spirits, liquor, wine, beer, and whisky. In China, the main ingredients name different wines—Bai-gan is a barley wine and Mi-joe (Japanese calls it Sake) is rice wine 米酒. They also can be named for the city where it is produced—Shou-sin is a very strong rice wine. Many tales were told that the Westerners got drunk because they thought that they were drinking wine, not spirits.

Chinese prefer to drink warm wine slowly with tidbits of delicacies and a pleasant conversation. There are many games to play when folks gathered together to have a drink. Simple ones of arithmetical competitions with fingers and fists are popular everywhere. When you see two or three Chinese men or women pointing the fingers or fists and shouting at each other, please don't think they are quarreling. They are having a good game and good time. The loser will have to drink.

For the sophisticated, a complicated game of word or verse association can be a real challenge and a brainteaser. Here the rules are different: only the winning party will have the honor to drink.

Realizing the huge profits of producing and distributing of this favorite beverage, the Chinese government controlled and monopolized the revenue from wine as early as the Han Dynasty (circa 200 B.C.), immediately after the Great Wall was built. Since then, the "wine" taxes collected are always an essential source of national budget.

The Chieftain, Pueblo, Colo., Sunday, January 8, 1995 Page 6E

Why history is so important to the Chinese

Succeeding the Red Emperor, the Yellow Emperor was the legendary and mystic first significant leader of China. Yellow Emperor invented compass and his queen discovered silkworms and silk. The Chinese civilization blossomed. This was the beginning of China. The Chinese called their nation Zhong Gho 中國– the kingdom of the center of the world.

China is not the world's oldest civilization, but it does have the longest continuous historical record of any community in the world. The record of the Chinese civilization is one of changes and evolution in an overall context of continuity for a period over 4000 years.

One of the important features of Chinese culture is the acute awareness of the importance of keeping historical records The meticulous attention to historical record keeping is almost as old as Chinese civilization itself. Scholars today could make use of the archives (in the form of bone or stone chips) preserved by the emperors of the Shang Dynasty. (Circa 2000 B.C.)

Every Dynasty had considered it a holy and serious obligation to compile an official history of the preceding dynasty. Every new emperor would have a sealed box similar to a huge piggy bank set up the first day he was on the throne. A group of assigned history record-keeping clerks would deposit into it almost daily the detailed record of the current affairs including the conversation between the emperor and his ministers. The box was sealed and the recoding clerk had the total frredowm to record the truth. Also because there

187

were more , at least 10, clerks to write, the record would be the truth. The histrical recording clerks of the next generation will open and sort out the records and to ceompile the history.

To the Chinese, the veneration of ancestors is a central feature of their culture. A record of past accomplishments and failures should be passed on to future generation.

The rulers of China believed that the emperors and the cultural heroes of the remote past provided the best available models for the people. Either the real or legendary remarkable achievements or faults of the past leaders would provide valuable guidance for the present and the future generation. The preservation of history is important to the Chinese.

The Chieftain, Pueblo, Colo., Sunday, March 22, 1992 page 3E

CPSIA information can be obtained
at www.ICGtesting.com
Printed in the USA
BVHW081047310521
608469BV00017B/395